EXPECT THE UNEXPECTED

EXPECT THE UNEXPECTED

HOW TO PREPARE YOUR FAMILY FOR TIMES OF EMERGENCY

American Red Cross

in conjunction with
MAXWELL HOUSE COFFEE®

Expect the Unexpected
How to Prepare Your Family for Times of Emergency

While every reasonable effort has been made to ensure the accuracy of this book, the American Red Cross, publisher of this information in conjunction with Maxwell House Coffee, and Lee Krost Associates, Inc., assume no responsibility or liability of any kind for its accuracy or completeness or for additional or changed information subsequent to the date the materials contained herein were submitted for publication.

This book was researched and prepared by M. Virginia Daly.

Introduction

When emergency strikes, will you be prepared? By taking the time now to "expect the unexpected" when the time comes, you will know how to handle the situation properly.

To help you prepare, this book was developed to assist you in handling natural disasters and many other emergencies.

You will learn how these disasters or emergencies may occur, how to prepare for them, what to do in times of need, and how to cope with the aftermath.

This is a serious reference book, and one that can be a valuable friend to you and your family.

In addition to being prepared for emergencies, you can make your community a better place to live. Support your local Red Cross Chapter or be a Red Cross Volunteer.

Preface

Many kinds of emergencies could involve you or any member of your family.

Fire. Flood. Hurricane. Cuts. Burns. No matter whether the emergency is large or small, you can cope far better if you are prepared. If, indeed, you "expect the unexpected." And know how to handle it.

For these situations seldom give warning and can be devastating to their victims.

This book was designed to help you understand these situations, how to react, and how—with proper preparation—to minimize the potential danger.

The time you take to read it now is an investment in future safety and protection to you and your family. And it is a book you will want to keep in a special place for reference.

Maxwell House and the American Red Cross are proud to be able to be of service to you and your family.

CONTENTS

Chapter 1

Emergency Preparedness

The Master Plan
    Checklist of Action Steps
    Designing the Master Plan

Home Emergency Supplies
    Survival
    Sanitation Supplies
    Safety and Comfort
    Tools and Related Supplies
    Cooking
    Car Mini-Survival Kit
    Identification

Specific Points on What to Know, What to Do Before, During, and After a Disaster
    Before a Disaster
    During and After a Disaster

How to Report an Emergency

What to Do if You Have to Evacuate

Tips on Safe Drinking Water
    How Much to Store
    How to Store Safe Water
    Emergency Sources for Safe Drinking Water
    How to Purify Water
Food Planning to Be Prepared for Disaster
    Two-Week Supply
    Tips for Emergency Food Storage and Nutrition
    Suggested Foods
    Cooking
    When the Electricity Is Off
    Guide for Reserve Food Supply

Chapter 2
Fire, Gas Leaks, and Blackouts

Chapter 3

Floods, Thunderstorms, and Lightning

Floods
    How to Prepare for Possible Floods
    Keep Alert
    Reaching Higher Ground
    After the Flood

Thunderstorms and Lightning
    "Killer" Lightning
    Tall Objects
    Heavy Rains
    Hail — the Underrated Hazard
    Aftermath of the Thunderstorm

Chapter 4

Dangers from Winter and Heat

Winter Dangers
    Wind-Chill Impact
    Protecting Yourself and Your Family
    Safe Return
    Protecting the Elderly
    More Cold-Weather Tips
    Cold-Weather Survival

Dangers from Heat
    Heat-Related illnesses
    Caring for the Elderly
    Ways to Beat a Heat Wave
    Making Air Conditioning More Effective
    What to do With *or Without* an Air Conditioner
    Dust Storms

Chapter 5

Earthquakes, Hurricanes, and Tornadoes

Earthquakes

Hurricanes

Tornadoes

Emergency Information

Emergency Information Sheets
    Fill Out Your Card
    Special Medical Problems
    Known Drug Allergies

Telephone Emergency Information Sheets

Sample Medical Releases for a Minor

Important Family Records

Important Telephone Numbers

First-Aid Kit for Your Automobile

House Diagram

Notes

Chapter 1
Emergency Preparedness

The Master Plan
    Checklist of Action Steps
    Designing the Master Plan

Home Emergency Supplies
    Survival
    Sanitation Supplies
    Safety and Comfort
    Tools and Related Supplies
    Cooking
    Car Mini-Survival Kit
    Identification

Specific Points on What to Know, What to Do Before, During, and After a Disaster
    Before a Disaster
    During and After a Disaster

How to Report an Emergency

What to Do if You Have to Evacuate

Tips on Safe Drinking Water
    How Much to Store
    How to Store Safe Water
    Emergency Sources for Safe Drinking Water
    How to Purify Water

Food Planning to Be Prepared for Disaster
    Two-Week Supply
    Tips for Emergency Food Storage and Nutrition
    Suggested Foods
    Cooking
    When the Electricity Is Off
    Guide for Reserve Food Supply

How to Prepare a First-Aid Kit
    Basic Items
    Nonprescription Drugs
    Bandages
    Additional Supplies
    Special Prescription Medications
    Storage

Can anyone really "expect the unexpected"? Yes, of course. What it truly means to expect the unexpected harkens back to the Boy Scout motto: "Be Prepared." While you might not know exactly what specific emergency to expect, you can indeed be prepared for all emergencies, any disaster. You can prepare yourself for anything. And for everything.

Being prepared, and being ready to provide those people you love most with the sort of help and protection you want them to have in times of critical emergency, take a little time and some advance planning. Time and trouble that could make the difference in saving or losing a life.

Use the following list of hazards as a checklist of possible threats that could affect you and your family:

- Floods   Virtually all areas of the United States are subject to flooding—like flash flooding or slow flooding.

- Thunderstorms and lightning   All parts of the United States are subject to this threat.

- Winter storms   Primarily cold-weather states, although southern states are occasionally subject to this threat.

- Heat   Primarily the southern United States, although all states are occasionally subject to heat waves.

- Earthquakes   Greatest threat exists in areas west of the Rocky Mountains, although midwestern states are significantly threatened as well.

- Hurricanes   Primarily Gulf and Atlantic Coastal areas. However, inland states often are affected by heavy rains and flooding resulting from hurricanes.

- Tornadoes   Virtually all midwestern states as well as the northeastern United States have significant numbers of these storms.

- Fire   The universal hazard, a threat to all communities. Fires affect more families every year than all the above hazards combined. A review of the chapters in this book will help you determine if you are at hazard.

The Master Plan

One of the primary things you can—and should—do before disaster strikes is to prepare yourself and your family for any eventuality. Create a *Master Plan* to cover all specifics within and outside your home that your family will need to know for times of emergency.

Evaluate which threats may affect you. Prioritize and examine those threats.

The Master Plan is one you should design, then review at least once a year with every single member of your family.

For purposes of planning, and throughout this book, the phrase "the family" is not limited to the traditional mother, father, and children. It could be taken to mean a "family" of roommates, a "family" of friends, a "family" of neighbors, or even a "family" in the sense of residents of an apartment building. It is a generic term used to mean those living in your close environs and with and for whom you share responsibility and concern.

The ranking of concerns for your family are: *Safety and health* are first; *concern for property* should be secondary.

Assign each family member the responsibility for a specific task that will be on the list in the Master Plan you create. In delegating such responsibility, also plan for family members to take Red Cross training in first aid and CPR.

In your planning, map out evacuation routes for different types of disaster, such as fire or flood. Drill your family members regularly on proper actions for various emergencies—for example, evacuating in case of fire, or taking shelter within the home in case of tornado. Also in your planning, think through and plan for the special needs of various people, such as infants, the elderly, or the chronically ill.

Ask and appoint a special out-of-town friend or relative to serve as your contact person if family members become separated during a disaster. This is key during daytime hours, when parents may be at the office and children at school. Make sure everyone knows who the contact person will be. Check to see if your designated person has a telephone number that's listed with the telephone company in case a family member needs to call Information to get the number. If that person keeps an unlisted number, appoint another contact person. Instruct family members to call that person for directions and emergency information. Also instruct younger members of your group how to call emergency Information. Select a location where you will meet members of your family should you become separated. Choose a main location with three or four alternative sites.

In regard to property, utility valves are important, for often in an emergency these need to be shut off immediately. Learn where they are and show them to every member of the family. Teach every responsible person in the household how to operate the valves properly. Keep the proper tools on hand to work the valves.

Include in your Master Plan a drawing of the floor plan of your home, noting escape routes, location of emergency supplies, and utility shutoffs.

File your Master Plan in a place that's easy to find, and review it regularly with your family and update it. Your birthday, the anniversary of the date you moved into your home, New Year's, or any easy-to-remember regular date is a good time to set aside for family meetings and disaster drills.

Checklist of Action Steps

Here's a handy checklist of action steps to take as part of your Master Plan:

- [ ] For minimum emergency equipment, get:
  - [ ] flashlight
  - [ ] radio, battery-operated
  - [ ] extra batteries for both
  - [ ] first-aid kit
  - [ ] an A-B-C-type fire extinguisher
- [ ] Maintain a minimum seventy-two-hour supply of food and water.
- [ ] Have extra prescription medicines and eyeglasses.
- [ ] Carry enough insurance of the right kind: homeowner's, renter's, fire, flood, etc.
- [ ] Be aware that not all general insurance policies cover damage from natural disasters.
- [ ] Store your important papers in a safe place, such as a safety deposit box or even your freezer. It is also a good idea to duplicate key documents.
- [ ] Keep immunizations current for all family members.
- [ ] Make a practice of keeping your auto gas tank half filled at all times to be ready for any contingency.
- [ ] Correct hazards around your home. For instance, strap down the water heater in earthquake-prone areas, or make sure cords for electrical appliances are properly placed to guard against fire.

Designing Your Master Plan

Your Master Plan should start with a drawing of your home's floor plan on a separate sheet of paper. Show the location of exit windows ∧ and doors ◄, utility cutoffs ●, first-aid kit +, emergency supplies □, food, clothing, tools, etc. Design and map out fire escape routes.

Make sure everyone in your household is familiar with your Master Plan. Share your plan with neighbors, friends, relatives, and coworkers. Show it to baby-sitters and houseguests when you're going to be away. They could use it to direct someone to a utility shutoff in an emergency.

See pages *123 & 124* sample floor plan & your emergency floor plan.

Home Emergency Supplies

Following are several lists of items usually available in a home and regularly used. These comprehensive lists are organized by category. This section is designed to help your family identify and organize materials for emergencies that may isolate your family at home for extended periods of time, such as flooding, blizzards, or earthquakes.

Quantities of emergency supplies should be adequate for at least seventy-two hours. A two-week supply is recommended as a minimum reserve of water, food, medicine, and other consumable items.

Survival

☐ Water: two quarts to one gallon of drinking water per person per day

☐ First-aid kit: ample and freshly stocked

☐ First-aid book: know how to use it

☐ Food: canned or dehydrated. Precooked and/or requiring minimum heat and water. Include foods that require no cooking, such as nuts, honey, dried fruit, and chocolate. Also consider infants, pets, and others who may have special dietary requirements.

☐ Can opener, nonelectric

☐ Blankets or sleeping bags for each member of the family

☐ Radio: portable, battery-operated; spare battery

☐ Essential medication and glasses, as required

☐ Fire extinguisher: A-B-C type

☐ Flashlight: fresh and spare batteries and bulbs

☐ Watch or clock: battery or spring-wound

☐ Escape ladder for two-story home or apartment

☐ Food for pets

☐ Money

Sanitation Supplies

- ☐ Large plastic trash bags: for trash, waste, water protection, ground cloth
- ☐ Large trash cans
- ☐ Hand soap
- ☐ Liquid detergent
- ☐ Shampoo
- ☐ Toothpaste and toothbrush
- ☐ Premoistened towelettes
- ☐ Deodorant
- ☐ Denture cleaner
- ☐ Feminine supplies
- ☐ Infant care supplies
- ☐ Toilet paper
- ☐ Newspapers: to wrap garbage and waste; also can be used for warmth
- ☐ Household bleach

Safety and Comfort

- ☐ Hat or cap: protection from sun, rain, or cold
- ☐ Sturdy shoes: for every family member
- ☐ Heavy gloves: for every person clearing debris
- ☐ Candles: check for gas leaks before using
- ☐ Matches: dipped in wax and kept in waterproof container
- ☐ Clothes: complete change kept dry
- ☐ Knife: sharp or razor blades
- ☐ Tent

Tools and Related Supplies

- ☐ Ax
- ☐ Shovel
- ☐ Broom
- ☐ Crescent wrench for turning off gas
- ☐ Screwdriver
- ☐ Pliers
- ☐ Hammer
- ☐ Coil of half-inch rope
- ☐ Plastic tape
- ☐ Pencil and paper
- ☐ Scissors
- ☐ Deck of cards, toys for children

Cooking

- [ ] Barbeque: charcoal and lighter, Sterno stock, or camp stove
- [ ] Plastic bags: various sizes, sealable
- [ ] Pots: at least two
- [ ] Paper plates and cups
- [ ] Plastic knives, forks, spoons
- [ ] Paper towels
- [ ] Heavy-duty aluminum foil
- [ ] Fuel for cooking equipment—charcoal, lighter fluid, fuel for camp stove, Presto logs

Car Mini-Survival Kit

- [ ] Nonperishable food: store in empty coffee cans
- [ ] Bottled water
- [ ] First-aid kit and book
- [ ] Flares
- [ ] Fire extinguisher, A-B-C type
- [ ] Blanket
- [ ] Sealable plastic bags
- [ ] Flashlight: fresh and spare batteries and bulbs
- [ ] Essential medication
- [ ] Tools: screwdriver, pliers, wire, knife, scissors
- [ ] Short rubber hose: for siphoning
- [ ] Small package of tissues
- [ ] Premoistened towelettes
- [ ] Paper and pencils
- [ ] Nylon cord
- [ ] Small metal mirror
- [ ] Whistle
- [ ] Walking shoes
- [ ] Phone money
- [ ] Local maps
- [ ] Extra clothing and shoes

Identification

Wallet I.D. with the following information (especially important for children):

- [ ] Blood type
- [ ] Medical problems (allergies, with current information)
- [ ] Prescription medication, (name, dosage, prescription number, and date prescribed)
- [ ] Eyeglass/contact lens preparation
- [ ] Doctor's name, address, and phone number
- [ ] Driver's license or other personal identification

Specific Points on What to Know, What to Do Before, During, and After a Disaster

Before a Disaster

Plan ahead. Here's what family members should know in advance of emergencies to use when time and circumstance allow. As always, personal safety comes first, property protection second.

1. Teach responsible members of your family to *turn off* electricity, gas, and water at the main switch and valves. Check with your local utility offices for instructions on what to do, and preplace the necessary tools to perform these functions.

2. Demonstrate and practice with family members when and how to escape and show them where the nearest safe shelter is.

3. Designate a particular place where your family members should meet in case you get separated.

4. Create a special, well-thought-out plan for the care of your beloved family pets.

5. Review safety precautions for different types of disasters. (See following chapters for specifics.)

6. Have members of your family trained in first aid and CPR instruction. If you need information about classes in these areas, call your Red Cross chapter.

7. Make sure to keep an extra flashlight, first-aid kit, battery-powered transistor radio (with extra batteries), and fire extinguisher in your home, ready for use at any time. Check them periodically (with each season) to be sure they are in good working condition.

8. Keep up to date on all immunizations for all family members.

9. Take the time to talk with your family about possible disasters. Do not tell frightening stories about disasters that could set the stage for panic, but rather make certain each family member knows about the preparations and can have a quick and confident response should an emergency occur.

10. Maintain a two- or three-day supply of food and water. You should have a minimum of one-half to two gallons of drinking water per day per person, stored in plastic jugs. It is also important to rotate your stock of food and water at least annually.

11. Keep your automobile fueled. If electric power is cut off, gas stations may not be able to operate their pumps for several days. Do not store gasoline in your garage or trunk.

12. Plan several different evacuation routes that deal with the threats of different disasters. In an actual emergency, listen to the Emergency Broadcast System on the radio for possible designated routes.

13. Twice a year conduct a "home hazard inspection." Make sure to repair immediately any hazards you identify.

14. Teach family members how to call for help (see following section for specifics).

15. Have family members learn disaster plans for schools and for companies employing family members.

16. Carry sufficient and appropriate insurance, such as home-owner's, renter's, fire, flood, and earthquake. It is recommended that you obtain a "replacement" rider if possible. Have comprehensive lists of all your possessions (backed up with photographs), including serial and model numbers. Keep these on file both on and off the premises in a safe place, such as a safety deposit box, with a relative or close friend. Be sure to include copies of important documents. If the following become destroyed, you will need to replace:

- Birth certificates
- Driver's license
- Bankbooks
- Insurance policies
- Credit cards
- Title to deeds
- Military discharge papers
- Passports
- Social Security cards
- Marriage and divorce papers
- Warranties
- Income-tax records
- Stocks and bonds
- Auto registration
- Auto title card
- Wills
- Prepaid burial contracts

17. Have extra prescription medicines and eyeglasses in storage, (the refrigerator is a good spot), as drugstores may be closed for several days and your doctor may be unreachable.

18. Arrange for a family member who is outside your area to serve as an "information center" to relay news about the welfare and location of family members in your area.

What to Do During and After a Disaster

1. First and foremost, *remain calm*. Think through the consequences of any action you take. Try to calm down, and reassure other members of your family.

2. Check for injuries to your family and neighbors. Do not attempt to move anyone who is seriously injured unless you feel they are in immediate danger of further injury.

3. Check for fires and fire hazards. Review all possible sources of fire.

4. Be sure to wear shoes in all areas that are near debris or broken glass. You do not want to injure yourself.

5. Never touch downed power lines or objects that are in contact with the downed wires.

6. If you have been evacuated, do not reenter your home unless public authorities have advised it is safe to return to the area. When reentering the home, check for damaged utilities:

   a. Inspect for leaky gas lines by smell only. *Do not* use candles, matches, or other open flames, and do not turn lights on or off. If you smell gas, open all windows and doors so gas can escape. Be sure to shut off the main valve at your gas meter, leave the house immediately, and notify authorities of the leak. Do not reenter the house until repairs are made and it is safe to enter. Do not turn the gas on until the repairs are completed.

   b. If water pipes are broken, shut off the main valve that brings water into the house.

   c. If damage to the electrical system is suspected (check for frayed wires, sparks, or the smell of hot insulation), turn off the system at the main circuit breaker or fuse box.

7. If the water is turned off, emergency water may be obtained from toilet tanks without chemicals, or from water heaters, melted ice cubes, and canned vegetables.

8. Before permitting continued flushing of toilets, check to see that sewage lines are intact.

9. If power is off, check to see what foods you have in your freezer, and plan meals to use up those foods that will spoil quickly.

10. For emergency cooking, use your outdoor charcoal broilers or camp stoves. Make sure the area around the cooker is properly vented. Do not use it in a closed area such as a tent or camper to prevent asphyxiation.

11. Keep your phone line clear. Do not use your telephone except for a genuine emergency call.

12. Be careful not to spread rumors. Keep wandering thoughts or speculation to yourself, as they can easily turn into rumors that can in turn cause great harm in a disaster.

13. Do not go "sightseeing." Keep the streets clear for the easy passage of emergency vehicles. Your presence might hamper rescue and other emergency operations.

14. Be responsive to requests for help from the police, fire fighters, civil defense, and Red Cross personnel. It is important to cooperate fully with public safety officials. Help them do their job helping you.

15. Tune your radio to the local Emergency Broadcast System stations for information, damage reports, and instructions.

16. Report broken utility lines to the appropriate authorities.

17. If you are not able to get in touch with the fire department for needed emergency medical treatment, go to the nearest hospital. First aid, as well as food, shelter, and clothing are also available at all Red Cross shelters.

18. Be sure to check periodically your emergency supplies to evaluate their condition. By knowing what your needs are, as well as what you have on hand, you can revise your plans accordingly.

19. For information about the welfare or location of separated family members, do not call or go to the police or fire departments.

20. If your fences or walls have been downed, be sure to figure out a way to confine pets, lest they get upset and possibly lost in the confusion.

21. After the disaster, contact your insurance agent as soon as possible and try to compile as comprehensive a list as possible of all your losses.

22. If you are not insured, or not fully insured, various governmental and nongovernmental agencies may be able to assist. Contact your local government officials and Red Cross chapter for assistance.

How to Report an Emergency

First and most important is to keep calm. When a fire, hurricane, earthquake, or other emergency happens, it is very hard to keep from getting overly excited. However, it is easier to think clearly when you remain calm. Take a few deep breaths and keep yourself calm.

Each member of your family should know to call your local emergency phone number to contact the ambulance. There are special sections in this book for special emergency numbers. Post other emergency phone numbers near or on each telephone.

When reporting an emergency:

1. Tell the dispatcher the type of emergency—fire, medical aid, etc.
2. Give your street address and street name, apartment building and unit, and city. The name of the complex also is helpful.
3. Give the nearest cross street to your address.
4. Give the phone number from which you are calling.
5. Stay on the line to answer any questions. *Do not* hang up the receiver until the person to whom you are speaking hangs up.
6. Speak slowly and clearly; hurry causes mistakes and misunderstandings.
7. Have someone at the street to guide the emergency vehicle to the scene when they arrive.
8. It is wise to have your address posted in a conspicuous place at all times, easily readable from the street. Your address numerals should be at least three inches high.

What to Do if You Have to Evacuate

If you have to evacuate your home, are you prepared? Have you thought through what you might need to take with you? Now is the time to give some concentrated thought to preparing your evacuation plan.

By preparing this list in advance now, when you are calm and collected, you will save precious time should an emergency occur.

Some of the things to take with you in case of evacuation include:
• Eyeglasses
• Dentures

- Hearing aids
- Prescription drugs
- Special foods (such as formula for an infant)
- Sturdy shoes, boots
- Raincoat, overcoat
- Favorite toy or blanket to comfort a child
- Children's I.D.
- Money: cash, checkbook, credit cards
- Driver's license
- Important papers
- Blankets, sleeping bag
- Extra clothing
- Keys
- First-aid kit
- Radio
- Food
- Water

If time allows for you to evacuate your home, remember to post a message in clear view—and in several obvious places— where you can be found. Also list the point and place of a reunion—with several alternatives—in case you and your family members become separated. Some likely meeting places include the homes of neighbors, friends, or relatives, a school or community shelter, or a Red Cross shelter.

In the same place that you keep your list of supplies should you need to evacuate, it is a good idea to keep some prepared cards with information about reunion places, addresses, and phone numbers.

And, as noted earlier, your "Master Plan" should include the name of an out-of-town person you and family members can contact in times of emergency. List that person's name and number along with the information about a local meeting spot.

When you evacuate, you need to move quickly. One way to take articles from the house when you're in a hurry is to put them in a large trash bag, or place a blanket on the floor, put the articles on it, gather up the four corners, and drag it from the house.

Moving quickly and calmly is paramount.

Some important telephone numbers you'll need in times of such emergency include:

- Fire department
- Police
- Ambulance
- Poison control center
- Doctor

Tips on Safe Drinking Water

The importance of having drinking water available that is safe cannot be underestimated. The human body is composed primarily of water, and it has been proven that you can survive several weeks without food—yet you can survive only a few days without water.

It is wise that you have on hand at all times a two-week supply of water for each member of your family. Reserve and store that water right now, while this book is in your hand, while the thought is on your mind.

How Much to Store

It takes at least one-half gallon of safe drinking water per day to supply the average needs of a normally active person during moderate weather. In times of emergency, some of that need for water can be met in other ways, such as using the juices from canned fruits and vegetables. In computing how much water to store per person for two weeks, also factor in that additional water will be required for bathing, brushing teeth, and washing dishes.

How to Store Safe Water

The large plastic gallon-size jugs that contain milk or juice are excellent for storing water. Also good are the five-gallon jugs available from water distributors. Mark the containers clearly with the date of storage. Put in your Master Plan to check the date of the emergency water supply, and plan to use it or discard it frequently.

Keep your reserve water in a cool, dark location.

Emergency Sources for
Safe Drinking Water

In coping with an emergency, just as you are learning to "expect the unexpected," you also must learn to discover the basic necessities in unexpected places. Such is the case with locating water. Some unexpected yet logical places to get water are from ice cubes, from your hot-water tank, and from your toilet tank (*not* the bowl). However, do not drink water from the toilet tank if a chemical disinfectant or purifier has been added to the water.

If using the hot-water tank as a source of water, to get a free flow of water it sometimes is necessary to open the valve at the top of the tank as well as the faucet at the bottom of the tank. You can also increase the flow of water if any hot-water faucet in your home is turned on before draining water from the hot-water tank.

Important note: Be sure to turn off the gas or electricity to the tank before you drain off water for your emergency use.

How to Purify Water

There are three basic methods of purifying water. Depending on the state of emergency you find yourself in, you can select from the following methods:

1. *Boiling water*
   Boil the water vigorously for one to three minutes. To improve the taste of the boiled water, pour it from one container to another several times.
2. *Water purification using tablets*
   You can purchase these tablets at any camping or sporting goods store as well as at a drugstore. If they are not out on the open shelf, ask the druggist for the tablets—sometimes they are stored behind the counter. They have a fairly long shelf life and are a good investment. They are useful especially for emergencies to sanitize potentially contaminated water that cannot be boiled. Follow the directions on the package of tablets.
3. *Water purification using bleach*
   The liquid household bleach you have on hand for laundry and cleaning can also be used. It must contain hypochlorite, preferably 5.25 percent.

Add bleach according to the following table, then stir and mix:

Amount of Water	Clear Water	Cloudy Water
1 quart	2 drops	4 drops
1 gallon	8 drops	16 drops
5 gallons	1/2 teaspoonful	1 teaspoonful

Food Planning to Be Prepared for Disaster

In America, in our time, it's easy to take it for granted that there's an adequate food supply. To change that perception, all it takes is one critical emergency, because disaster can dramatically disrupt the food supply at any time.

The emergency or disaster may be localized or it may be widespread. It may be as major as an earthquake—or as seemingly minor as a blocked road, or perhaps a water main failure. Whatever form the emergency takes, it is good to have a supply of emergency foods on hand, as the same material in your reserve supply will serve you in any situation.

Your supply of emergency rations can be made up of those foods your family prefers in meals every day. There is no need to rush out and buy large supplies of food you have never even tried. No special foods are necessary—rather, the canned foods, dry mixes, and the other staples you have on your cupboard shelves are well suited to emergency plans.

Not only does using foods your family regularly enjoys make preparation for emergencies easier, but also using foods that are familiar is important. The familiar can lift morale and give family members a feeling of security in times of stress.

Two-Week Supply

The minimum emergency food you need is a supply for two weeks. Even though you probably won't be on your own for that long, prepare an amount that can carry you through. Your two-week supply of water and food can go a long way toward relieving a great deal of inconvenience and uncertainty during the immediate postdisaster period until you have orderly services and systems restored to you. Evaluate your particular needs based on the chart on hazards earlier in this chapter.

Right now you may already have a two-week supply of food on hand in your pantry or on the cupboard shelves. Check it out to reassure yourself. To maintain that reserve is a simple matter of use and replacement.

In the area of safety, commercially canned foods will keep almost indefinitely, as long as the cans are not leaking or bulging. However, your emergency food supply should be of the highest quality possible. This means good color, flavor, and appearance. Considering this, it is optimum if you rotate the supply once or twice a year.

Tips for Emergency Food Storage and Nutrition

• Make it a rule to eat at least one square meal a day.
• Drink adequate amounts of liquid—water, soup, juices, beverages—to enable your body to function properly.
• Variety may be limited, but calories should be ample to meet energy needs and to provide the protein to do important work.
• In your disaster planning, experiment by serving your family a meal from a "disaster" menu. Practice by serving your family a disaster meal once a month so they will be familiar with survival food preparation.
• Choose foods your family likes.
• Keep food in the driest and coolest spot in the house, and choose a dark area if possible.
• Keep food covered at all times.
• Open food boxes or cans carefully so that you can close them tightly after each use.
• Wrap bread, cookies, or crackers in plastic bags and keep them in tight containers.
• Empty opened packages of sugar, dried fruits, or nuts into screw-top jars or airtight tin cans because insects and rodents may be a problem.
• Don't forget canned and nonperishable foods for your beloved pets!
• Foods in glass bottles and jars may break when a disaster occurs. Buy emergency foods in cans whenever possible.

Suggested Foods

The following items have a fairly long shelf life and are suggested for disaster and emergency use, as they need no refrigeration before opening:
• Canned protein foods: tuna, lunch meat, ham, beef, chicken, salmon, sardines
• Canned vegetables: green beans, corn, carrots, peas, spinach, beets, sweet potatoes, pumpkin, turnip greens, etc.
• Canned fruits: applesauce, pineapple, fruit cocktail, pears, apricots, peaches, plums, etc.
• Fresh fruits: apples, bananas, grapefruit, oranges, lemons, grapes, apricots
The following foods might also be kept on hand (note that not all of them have a long shelf life):
• Sweets and nuts, dried fruits, seeds, raisins, prunes, peanuts, assorted nuts, sunflower seeds, etc.

- Nonfat or low-fat milk; evaporated milk if used within one day after opening and kept at cool room temperature
- Teabags; instant tea, coffee, or cocoa; fruit juices
- Peanut butter
- Jelly, jams, preserves, honey, molasses
- Small chunks of hard cheese, if used within a few days
- Bread wrapped in its original wrapping
- Dry, crisp crackers in metal container
- Ready-to-eat cereals
- Oatmeal cookies or crackers
- Salt, pepper, sugar, seasonings
- Bouillon, flavored beverages
- Flavored extracts, soda, baking powder
- Hydrogenated fats, vegetable oils
- Margarine in container
- Catsup or prepared mustard
- Instant puddings

Cooking

Often in a disaster situation one of the first things to go is the electricity. Then you're stuck with no gas or electricity for cooking. But by learning to look to the unexpected, you can use a charcoal grill, hibachi, or camp stove for necessary cooking.

Remember: Such cooking is for *outdoors only*!

You'll also be able to heat food with candle warmers, chafing dishes, or even fondue pots. Just as campers do, you can heat canned food in the can, but be sure to remove the paper label and open the can first.

When the Electricity Is Off

1. Use perishable foods and foods from the refrigerator first.
2. Use foods from the freezer. Keep a list of freezer foods on the outside, so you can cut down on the number of times you have to open the freezer door. Foods in a well-filled, well-insulated freezer do not begin to spoil as quickly. Usually there will still be ice crystals in the center of the foods for at least three days after a power failure—so you know they are safe to eat. If in doubt, do not use the food.
3. Begin to use nonperishable foods and staples.

Guide for Reserve Food Supply

Amount per adult for:

Kind of Food	1 Day	2 Weeks	Remarks
Milk	Equivalent of 2 (8-oz.) glasses fluid	Equivalent of 7 qts. fluid	7 qts. = 8 tall cans of evaporated milk or 1½ lbs. of nonfat dry milk
Commercially canned meat, poultry, fish, cooked dry beans, peas	2 servings	28 servings (8–9 lbs.)	One serving is: Canned meat, poultry, fish: 2–3 ozs. Canned mixtures of meat, fish, poultry with vegetables, rice, macaroni, spaghetti, noodles, or cooked dry beans: 8 ozs. Condensed soups containing meat, poultry, fish, or dry beans or dry peas: ½ of 10½-oz. can
Fruits and vegetables	3–4 servings	42–56 servings (about 21 lbs. canned)	One serving is: Canned juices: 4–6 ozs. single strength Canned fruits or vegetables: 4 ozs. Dried fruits: 1½ ozs. Examples: orange, grapefruit, tomato juice; oranges, grapefruit, apples, bananas, apricots; carrots, yams, pumpkins, potatoes, corn, spinach, turnip greens, kale, prunes, raisins
Cereals and baked goods	3–4 servings	42–56 servings (5–7 lbs.)	One serving is: Breads, rolls, pancakes: 1 Cereals, ready-to-eat: ½–1 oz. Crackers, quick-cook cereals: 1 oz. Cookies: 1 oz. Flour mixes: 1 oz. Macaroni, spaghetti, noodles, rice: dry, ¾ oz.; canned, 6 ozs.

Kind of Food	1 Day	2 Weeks	Remarks
Spreads for bread and crackers	According to individual practices	Up to 1 lb.	Examples: cheese spreads, peanut and other nut butters; jams, jellies, marmalades, preserves, syrups, honey, apple, and other fruit butters; relishes, catsup, mustard, mayonnaise
Fats and oils		1 lb. or 1 pt.	Kinds of fats and oils that need no refrigeration; amount depends on extent of cooking possible
Sugars, sweets, nuts, and seeds		1–2 lbs.	Examples: sugar, hard candy, nuts, seeds, instant puddings
Miscellaneous	According to individual practices and extent of cooking possible		Examples: coffee, tea, cocoa (instant), bouillon products, flavored beverage powders, salt and pepper, other seasonings, vinegar, soda, baking powders

It is important to remember to make special food plans for elderly or ill persons. A supply of special canned dietetic foods, strained or chopped foods, juices, and soups may be helpful.

Teenagers may need more than the amounts recommended in the table; younger children may need less.

Select a variety from each food group. Plan for more than needed. Use portions of food not required by infant for adult's snacks.

How to Prepare a First-Aid Kit

Your first-aid kit can be created in any manner you like—plain or fancy. In a velvet-covered box . . . a wicker basket . . . or an old shoe box. The only real requirement is that it be created.

And when you create it, it should be tailored to fit the needs of your own family.

For many, a small cardboard box with a lid works very well as a container. Other suggestions are to use a fishing tackle box . . . a cosmetics case . . . or a tool box. Whatever shape it may take, keep the box in an easily accessible place—but one that is out of reach of small children! Remember special needs for special folks in your family, such as an extra pair of eye-glasses, toys for children, sugar for a diabetic, allergy relief, etc.

Basic First-Aid-Kit Items

The following items are recommended as basic items for a family first-aid kit:

- Sterilized gauze squares (assorted sizes—two, three, four inches)
- Roller gauze (one each of one, two, and three inches)
- Plain absorbent gauze pads (one eighteen-inch, one twenty-four-by-seventy-two inches)
- Eyepads
- Triangular bandages (three)
- Packet of assorted adhesive dressing (such as Band-Aids)
- Roll of adhesive tape (one-half inch or one inch wide)
- Pair of small scissors
- Pair of tweezers
- Thermometers (one oral, one rectal)
- Tongue blades and wooden applicator sticks
- Tube of petroleum jelly or other lubricant
- Assorted sizes of safety pins
- Cleansing agent — soap
- First-aid book

Nonprescription Drugs

You may want to get a list of preferred drugs and supplies from your family health professional. Some of the items to be considered and recommended include:

- Aspirin or acetaminophen (such as Tylenol) to reduce fever or pain
- Antidiarrhea medication
- Antacid (for stomach upset)

- Emetic (to induce vomiting following poisoning)
- Laxative (the addition of fresh and dried fruits to the diet is also helpful)
- Eyewash (large amounts of water work best)
- Alcohol
- Vitamin supplements

Bandages

You can make bandages rather easily from sheets torn into strips. You can also use clean rags, disposable diapers, or sanitary pads. Dressings can be held in place by using these strips, or by using men's ties, plastic bags, or nylon stockings. Be creative and improvise when necessary. As you're planning to "expect the unexpected," you can also learn to use regular household items in unexpected, useful ways.

Additional Supplies

Some additional items that you and your family might find helpful include:

- Plastic bags, small and large
- Paper cups
- Spoons
- Needle and thread
- Splinting material
- Disposable diapers
- Sanitary napkins
- Formula
- Medicine dripper
- Cotton-tipped swabs
- Cold packs
- Hot packs
- Cotton
- Tissues
- Salt
- Baking soda
- Matches
- Premoistened towelettes
- Hand lotion
- Pocket knife
- Elastic bandage
- Extra eyeglasses
- Contact lenses and supplies
- Sunscreen lotion

Special Prescription Medications

It is recommended that you contact your personal physician for recommendation of specific prescription medicines such as:

• Insulin
• Heart medication
• High-blood-pressure medication
• Other essential medication

It is also wise to obtain specific information from your physician or pharmacist on labeling, storage, how much to store, how often to rotate, etc., for your prescription medications. Some medications have a longer "shelf life" than others, and it is worthwhile to keep track of what you and your family will need.

Storage of Your First-Aid Kit

Keep your first-aid kit in an easily accessible place—but keep it out of the reach of children. It is not meant for play.

Be sure to keep a list of contents taped to the lid of the box.

Periodically check the contents, and restock those supplies that have been used or are out of date.

Chapter 2
Fire, Gas Leaks, and Blackouts

 Fire

Fire is a tool, not a toy. Fire can even be useful in putting out a fire—thus the adage fighting fire with fire. And, while some fires begin "naturally," such as with lightning, most often fires are manmade and therefore preventable.

Unfortunately, many of us are lax in using the most effective means of fire fighting—fire prevention education and fire exit drills. As a result, fire is among the leading causes of accidental deaths in the home each year.

The statistics are staggering: In the United States, someone dies in a fire every forty minutes, with countless others being

maimed or disfigured. Most often these victims are children
and the elderly. In addition, fires are responsible for over two
billion dollars' worth of damage to homes annually.

The leading cause of fire deaths is asphyxiation, not flames.
Fire quickly consumes oxygen in the air, thereby increasing the
carbon monoxide concentration in the air. In addition to the
inhalation of smoke and noxious fumes, superheated air or
gases will result in loss of consciousness or death within minutes after temperatures rise to three hundred degrees Fahrenheit or higher. Therefore, immediate response to a fire is
absolutely essential.

How to Prepare for a Fire

In addition to being the third-largest accidental killer in the
nation, fire is the most likely disaster you and your family are
apt to experience. Furthermore, over 80 percent of all fire
deaths occur *where* people sleep—in homes, apartments,
motels, hotels, and mobile homes. In addition, most fires
occur *when* people are sleeping—between midnight and morning, when people are less alert. Therefore, it is important that
fire safety techniques and escape plans be practiced often
enough to become "second nature" to each and every member
of your family.

Fire Prevention: The First Step in
Fire Safety

Every room in your home is a potential fire hazard. Therefore, it's important that you and your family be alert to the
potential dangers. The key is to prevent, not put out fires!

Kitchen Safety

All electrical appliances and tools should have a testing
agency label (UL for Underwriters Laboratories, or FM for
Factory Mutual). Electrical appliances (other than ovens, dishwashers, and refrigerators) should be unplugged when not in
use and the cords and plugs checked for wear. Frayed, worn
cords or plugs should be replaced or repaired. Furthermore, if
there is any evidence that an electrical appliance is not working
properly, make sure it is not used again until it is repaired.

Electrical kitchen appliances pose two additional hazards.
The first is electrical shock. When water and electricity are
combined, shock will result. In addition to receiving a painful
reminder, shock also can result in an electrical fire. Therefore,

follow the three basic rules for operating electrical appliances in the kitchen: (1) Thoroughly dry hands before operating appliances, switches, and outlets in the kitchen. (2) Don't stand in water while operating these devices. (3) Have an appliance repaired if it gets wet.

The other electrical appliance hazard is the overloading of outlets. It is important that you not use all electrical appliances at the same time, and never plug more appliances into a socket than it is designed to accommodate with safety. If overloading occurs, locate the source of the problem before replacing a fuse or repositioning a tripped circuit breaker. Furthermore, always use the correctly rated fuse in the fuse box, and NEVER try to replace a blown fuse with a penny or other makeshift fuse substitute. If there is any smoke coming from an electric motor or appliance, immediately pull the plug or turn off the power supply by tripping the circuit breaker or pulling the fuse.

Other important fire prevention rules for kitchen safety include:
- Store only infrequently used or nonflammable items over the stove. Not only can the substances catch fire, but also people often get burned reaching.
- Wear tight sleeves when you cook, since loose-fitting garments can catch fire.
- Turn pot handles inward so children can't pull them down.
- Make certain you fully understand how to relight the pilot on a gas range.
- Have an appropriate fire extinguisher on a wall away from the stove.
- It can also help to have baking soda close to the stove in the event of a grease fire. Or you may wish to cover a pot or skillet burning on the range, since fire needs oxygen to burn. Remember to turn off the power or gas whether the fire is in the oven or the top burners.
- Dust around stoves, refrigerators, and dishwashers periodically, since the small spark emitted when these electrical appliances are turned on can ignite any accumulated dust.

Living Rooms and Dens

One of the first rules for fire safety in the family rooms is that where there are *smokers*, there can be fire! Thus make sure there is an ample supply of ashtrays when smokers are present. These ashtrays should be large and, preferably, be designed with the cigarette holders in the center of the tray, since cigarettes and cigars can burn down and drop off the edge if the holders are on the lip of the ashtray. However, care should also be taken that no smoking materials are left to burn for any reason.

In addition, before going to bed, look under cushions, couches, and chairs for any smoldering cigarettes. Not only is there a risk of fire, but also many fabrics produce toxic gases when burning. Also be particularly careful about emptying ashtrays before bed—the toilet, never the wastebasket, since all it takes is one hot ash.

The fireplace is another common fire hazard, requiring particular caution. Make sure the flue is completely open before lighting a fire and that the fireplace screen is either metal or glass. It is also wise to make sure that carpets and furnishings are a safe distance from the hearth and are made with fire-retardant materials as well. When starting the fire, use kindling instead of paper, and burn only wood or manmade logs—NEVER charcoal. And finally, have your chimney checked and cleaned regularly, especially if manmade logs are used, since creosote is one of the components of these manmade materials and will build up in the chimney, closing off the draft. (See the special section on fireplace safety in this chapter.)

Portable heaters may make family rooms cozier, but they also pose fire hazards if improperly used. Keep these devices away from people and combustibles such as drapes, couches, etc. But first and foremost, use only the type and grade of fuel designated by the manufacturer. For electric portable heaters, only those with automatic shutoffs should be used.

Although some fire safety rules are self-explanatory—such as the rule on keeping lighters and matches where small children cannot reach them—others may not be quite as self-evident. For example, special outlet covers should be used to keep children's fingers out, and never leave an extension cord ungrounded, since a child could put the live end in his or her mouth and suffer severe burns.

In addition, fire safety in the family rooms should include:
- Make certain that the television, stereo, and other electronic devices won't overheat due to lack of sufficient air space.
- TV antennas should be insulated and grounded to protect against lightning.
- Electric cords should not be run under carpets or hooked over nails.

Bedrooms and Bathrooms

The hard and fast fire safety rule is never to smoke in *bed*. Indeed, it is strongly suggested that people not smoke in *bedrooms or bathrooms*, since such seemingly harmless activities as smoking while using hair spray can be extremely hazardous.

In addition, care should be taken in the bathroom while using electricity: Remember that water and electricity produce shock.

Particular care should also be taken that children's clothing and bedding be fire-retardant!

Basement, Garage, and Storage Areas

These particular areas of the home often are the most hazardous, often a collector's dream and a fire fighter's nightmare. Here most people store gasoline, solvents, and other flammable liquids; haphazardly stash old clothing and memorabilia; and use their workbench, often leaving sawdust and wood chips in their wake. And quite often these areas also are the site of the heating equipment.

Fire safety in these areas is particularly important and should include:

- Storage of gasoline and other flammables in tight metal containers, preferably away from the house and NEVER near the heating equipment, a pilot light, or while smoking.
- Trash should be sorted and removed. Items to be saved should never be stored near the furnace or water heater. (*Helpful Hint*: Many of these items can be stored in plastic or metal garbage cans, which are airtight as well as fire-retardant.)
- Have heating equipment checked annually.
- Keep flammables away from sparks when using your workbench, and make sure to clean the workbench area after each use.
- If a fuse blows or the lights go out, find the cause and correct it before replacing the fuse or tripping the circuit breaker. (Replace the fuse with one of the correct size and amperage.)

Wood- and Coal-Burning Stoves

Although coal-burning stoves are no longer common, they still are used in some sections of the country. Since the energy crisis in the 1970s, however, wood-burning stoves have again become popular. There are several safety tips that should be followed when using either heating device:

- Make sure the stoves are properly vented to the outside of the home, and keep a window slightly open while in use to provide enough oxygen for proper combustion and to prevent carbon monoxide poisoning.
- Allow plenty of clearance between your wood stove and walls, curtains, and furniture. NEVER keep kindling, newspapers, or other flammable materials near the stove.
- NEVER store or use gasoline or other flammable liquids in the same room with the stove, and NEVER use any of these fuels to start a fire.
- Use the proper fuel:
  1. To prevent overheating, don't use coal, charcoal, plastic, or paper products in a wood-burning stove.
  2. To prevent explosions, don't use flammable liquids on a wood or coal fire.
  3. Don't use charcoal or other fuels not intended for use in open stoves or fireplaces, in order to prevent carbon monoxide poisoning.
- Try to keep a fire at a moderate heat, neither too cool nor too hot. If the fire is too low, creosote may build up in the chimney, causing a fire. A low flame also may cause moisture to condense in the flue and lead to corrosion of metal parts.
- A glowing-red stovepipe is equally dangerous. Never stoke up a fire so hot that it changes the color of the stovepipe. Cool the fire quickly by closing the stove dampers and partially closing the stovepipe damper. If that doesn't cool it fast enough, put a few shovelsful of ashes on top of the burning wood or coal.
- Ashes should NEVER be transferred from the stove to a cardboard box. Hot ashes may be "live" for more than twenty-four hours and can cause delayed fires. Place ashes in metal containers ONLY, and discard when cool.
- Don't hang clothes near the stove to dry, since they may catch fire.
- Educate your whole family in the *safe* use of a stove or fireplace. But ALWAYS keep small children away from stoves, because they can be burned simply by touching the hot surface.

Fireplace Safety Checklist

When done safely, sitting before a roaring fire in the fireplace will warm home and heart. But without the proper safety precautions, it could be a heartbreaker!

The first rule of thumb is to make certain that the fireplace was meant to be used as a fireplace. Sound silly? You'd be amazed at how many "fireplaces" were designed for decoration—not fires!

Once you've determined that the fireplace is usable:

- Open the damper (flue) before lighting a fire.
- Check regularly to make sure that all vents and chimneys are clean and operating properly. This is particularly important if you frequently use manmade logs, since creosote will build up in the chimney, closing off the flue.
- Don't use too much paper to start a fire. Instead, rely on kindling—NEVER gasoline or flammable liquids.
- Burn only proper firewood, not trash.
- Always use a metal screen or glass fire doors to prevent sparks from escaping into the room.
- NEVER burn charcoal in a fireplace (or anywhere else indoors), since charcoal can give off deadly amounts of carbon monoxide.
- Follow package directions if you use manmade logs. NEVER break a manmade log apart to quicken the fire.
- Dispose of ashes properly—outside, in a metal container with a tight-fitting lid.
- NEVER close the damper with hot ashes in the grate. A closed damper will cause smoke or allow heat buildup, causing ashes to flare up again.
- Don't decorate the mantel with flammable materials, to prevent sparks from igniting them and starting a fire.

Christmas Tree Safety

'Tis the season for decking the halls and lighting the Christmas tree. Unfortunately, that's when 'tis also the season for fires, many of them stemming from the tree itself, whether natural or artificial.

Natural-tree safety reminders:

- Use a freshly cut tree. Since trees begin losing water within minutes of cutting, do not accept the salesman's word for the tree's freshness. Even when cutting your own tree, moisture will be lost in the trek home. Therefore, cut a section off from the trunk before putting it into the base. Then fill the base with water, replenishing the water *daily*.
- The Christmas tree should be on display for *no more than* two weeks. Once it is taken down, get rid of it immediately.
- Place trees away from stairways and such heat sources as fireplaces, radiators, room heaters, etc., which would dry

out the tree and increase the danger of fire. Trees should never block hallways, doorways, or exits to prevent escape.

- Never allow open flames, such as candles, near a tree.
- If electric lights are used to trim a tree, inspect them to make sure they have laboratory approval and have no frayed wires or other defects before installing them.
- Toys, trains, or any device that generates sparks should be kept away from the tree.
- When lit, the tree should not be left alone. All electrical decorations should be disconnected at night or when leaving the house.
- Use only noncombustible decorations such as tinsel, being especially careful with spray and "angel hair" decorations.
- Fire retardants, whether homemade or commercial, might not be fully effective if applied to only part of the tree.
 Artificial-tree safety measures:
- Do not use electric lights on metal trees.
- If not made of metal, the artificial tree should be noncombustible. Check for the testing laboratory label to make sure the entire tree—trunk, trunk wrapping, and branches—are noncombustible.
- Miniature lights can be used with some artificial trees. Follow the tree manufacturer's instructions carefully. Minilights also should have a laboratory testing label.

When Fire Occurs

When you and your family are thoroughly familiar with all the fire safety measures needed and are assured that all preventative measures have been taken, you must then fully prepare yourself to act if a fire does occur. Remember, fire is the most common disaster you or your family will experience, and a timely response to this killer can spell the difference between safety and casualties.

There are two major tools to avoid tragedies of death and disfigurement in the event of a fire:

1. escape plans and drills
2. fire safety equipment

Designing an Escape Plan

An escape plan must be devised *before* a fire occurs. The sample floor plan in Chapter 1 can be used to help you create your own plan. This plan should have special provisions for infants, elderly, or handicapped persons. Once the plan itself is devised, it should be discussed with all members of your household until you are convinced that everyone understands what needs to be done. Then have regular exit drills to make sure everyone can put the plan into practice.

STEPS TO SAFETY. You and, subsequently, each member of your family should walk through the main escape route several times. Since most fires occur between midnight and morning light, practice in the dark or with your eyes closed. Try to have everyone memorize the number of steps between obstacles or turns. And if a piece of furniture keeps getting in the way, move it.

You must plan alternate routes of escape from each room. If bedroom windows are too high for safe jumping, perhaps you should buy a rope or chain escape ladder to keep at the window of each bedroom.

If you must go through a smoke-filled area, crawl on hands and knees with your head low to avoid breathing smoke. Furthermore, before opening an inside door, touch the knob and the top of the door. If either is hot, do not open the door, since fire on the other side might flash into your room. Instead, use your secondary route.

If the fire seems to be localized in one room, if possible, close the door, since it will help contain the fire and delay its spread to hallways or adjoining rooms.

Escape first. Call later. Precious moments can be lost if you call the fire department or 911 from a burning home. Instead, get out safely, then telephone from a neighbor's home or an alarm box.

Your escape plan should include a place outside where you and your family will meet. This will enable you to make sure everyone is out safely.

Do not return to the house or apartment under any circumstances until the fire fighters have assured you that the fire is fully extinguished and the structure is sound.

Fire Safety Equipment

There are two basic devices that no home should be without: smoke detectors and fire extinguishers. Both may save your life. The latter may also save your home.

Smoke Detectors: Your Early-Warning System

Since most fire deaths are caused by asphyxiation, and usually at times when people are sleeping, smoke detectors are the most effective piece of fire fighting equipment you have in your home. They are so necessary that the National Fire Protection Association recommends them for all newly constructed homes and public buildings, stating that "smoke detectors shall be installed outside of each separate sleeping area in the immediate vicinity of the bedrooms and on each additional story of the family living unit, including basements (but excluding crawl spaces and unfinished attics)." Additionally, many local jurisdictions mandate their installation in all residences, new or old.

Where sleeping rooms are on an upper level, a detector should also be placed in the center of the ceiling directly above the stairway. However, avoid installation in bathrooms and in areas exposed to heating and air-conditioning vents.

After installation, smoke detectors must be maintained. It is recommended that each smoke detector be tested once a month, without fail, to replace dead batteries and to clean away any dust or cobwebs from the face of the detector.

There are many different types of smoke detectors. You want a reliable one. This does not mean that it has to be expensive, but it should bear the notice that it is approved by UL (Underwriters Laboratory), FM (Factory Mutual), or by your state fire marshal.

The A-B-C's of Fire Extinguishers

When correctly used, fire extinguishers can keep small fires from becoming big ones, provide an escape route through a small fire, and help fight a small fire until the fire department arrives. However, if there ever is a question of whether to put it out or get out, opt for safety.

Since there are three major classes of fires, there are also three different types of fire extinguishers:

Ordinary combustibles (paper, cloth, wood, rubber, many plastics).	Use an extinguisher with the green "A" symbol on the label.
Flammable liquids (oils, gasoline, kitchen greases, paints, solvents).	Use an extinguisher with the red "B" symbol on the label.

| Electrical equipment (for wiring fires, fuse boxes, motors, power tools, appliances). | Use an extinguisher labeled with a blue "C" symbol. |

There is also a multipurpose dry chemical extinguisher labeled A-B-C that is effective in putting out most types of fires. Your local fire department will be pleased to recommend the proper types, sizes, and numbers of extinguishers for your home.

To be safe and effective, however, the fire extinguisher must be accessible *and* must be operated by someone who knows how to use it. Again, your local fire department can be most helpful in suggesting mounting instructions for your home and instructing you in the fire extinguisher's use.

For simple operating instructions, remember the word "P-A-S-S":

P for Pull: Pull the pin or ring (some units require release of a lock latch, pressing a puncture lever or other motion).

A for Aim: Aim the extinguisher at the *base* of the fire.

S for Squeeze: Squeeze or press the handle.

S for Sweep: Sweep from side to side slowly at the base of the fire until it goes out.

All members of the family should be instructed in the use of fire extinguishers. These instructions and operations should also be periodically reviewed. However, these instructions are not complete unless each family member fully understands that if the fire begins to spread or get bigger, *get out*!

As mentioned before, in the tips for kitchen safety, baking soda is very effective for extinguishing cooking fires. There also are other ordinary household items that are useful in extinguishing small, localized fires. To name a few:

• Garden hoses for extinguishing ordinary combustibles. Hoses should be connected at all times and provided with an adjustable nozzle. They should reach all sections of the house. (It is also recommended that a hose be provided for both the front and the rear of the house.)
• Buckets and similar containers should be kept near water sources.
• A shovel is very handy for small outdoor areas that can be controlled by spreading or throwing dirt.

Fire Caution Outdoors

Whether camping, barbecueing, or burning leaves, fire can pose a severe threat to life and limb, your property, or your neighbors' property. Therefore, extreme caution must be used.

Campfires

Since many campsites are inaccessible to fire fighters, the camper has a responsibility to exercise both judgment *and* caution when lighting (and, ultimately, dousing) a campfire. Campfires should be built in designated areas using provided grills. If building an open fire, surround the fire with rocks or dirt, and keep a bucket of water or dirt handy. Make sure all fires are thoroughly out before retiring or leaving the site, since embers can burn for hours. Be extremely careful of wind direction, and make certain that there is no nearby brush or trees.

Barbecues

For the standard grill, follow instructions for using charcoal lighter fluids carefully. Otherwise there is a high risk of fire. NEVER pour charcoal fluid or any other highly flammable fuel directly onto coals that have already been ignited, due to a chance that smoldering coal may flare up or explode. To brighten a barbecue fire that is dying down, first pour a small amount of lighter fluid on a few pieces of charcoal (do it away from the fire!) and *then* add the pieces to the fire carefully— one piece at a time.

If using an electric starter, remember that water and electricity cause shock and sometimes fire. Therefore, outdoor chefs should be cautious when plugging the starter into an outlet, being careful that the ground is not damp or that they are not standing in water. ALWAYS use an insulated indoor/outdoor cord. Furthermore, when removing the fire starter, make sure it is placed on a nonflammable object or table that cannot be reached by children, since the heating element will remain hot for several minutes after the red color goes out of the coil, causing fire and/or severe burns.

With gas grills, read all installation and operating instructions provided by the manufacturer, being careful to use the exact type of tank and fuel specified. Should the electric starter fail, use extreme caution trying to relight a pilot, since escaping gas can cause an explosion.

Burning Leaves

Most communities now forbid the burning of leaves because of the high risk of both fire and smoke damage. In areas where this practice still is permitted, leaves should be burned in areas away from the house, brush, or trees—preferably on cement. Also, leaves should be burned in small, controllable quantities, since this type of fire can easily spread, and wind conditions change. Make sure there is ample water supply to douse the embers when burning is complete.

Fire Safety Tips for Travelers

Although most fires occur in places where people sleep, these fires are not restricted to the home or apartment. Indeed, some of the most disastrous fires in history have occurred in hotels, motels, and motorized campers, where fire poses a threat to sometimes hundreds of people. Remembering the following instructions could help you remain safe should a fire occur at the hotel or motel in which you are staying.

- When making reservations or upon arrival at the facility, inquire about hotel/motel fire precautions.
- Locate fire doors in both directions—that is, count the number of doors from your room to the fire exits nearest you in *both* directions. Check for obstructions such as chairs or tables, and also note corners.
- Check fire exits. Do they open? Do they open to the outside of the building? Are they clear or blocked open?
- When you get to your room, note windows. Do they operate? Where do they lead?
- Check for posted instructions. Make sure it is marked correctly, since sometimes room charts are backward or upside down.

- Make sure there is a smoke alarm in the room and that it is operational. (Most smoke alarms have a glowing red light to show they are working. If the red light is flashing, notify the desk, since the blinking light usually indicates that the batteries need replacement.) Also know the location of fire extinguishers.
- Keep your key and billfold near you at all times (on the bedside stand, on top of the TV, etc.). Purchase a small pen flashlight and roll of two-inch masking tape (to tape the door if you're forced to stay in the room) to carry with you on each trip.

If a fire breaks out in your room, take your key and leave your room immediately, closing the door behind you. Pull the nearest fire alarm and, if there is time, knock on doors near you to alert people. Then proceed to the nearest fire exit, using the stairs to go to the ground level. NEVER take the elevator when there is a fire, since you may be trapped if the elevator stops. Remember, most fire-related deaths are due to asphyxiation, not the fire itself.

If you are notified of a fire in the hotel, follow posted emergency instructions. Usually you will be instructed to:

- Take your key and go to your door. Use your hand to check the temperature of the door. If it is hot, do not open it. Instead, assume that you are trapped in your room.
- If the door is cool, place your foot at the base of the door, one hand on the knob and the other bracing the door. Open just a crack, and check for smoke or heat. If no smoke is in the air, move to the exit and proceed down the steps and outside.
- If no stairs are clear, return to your room. If the hall is hazy, crawl down the hall, counting the doors to the nearest exit.
- Do not jump from high windows, and NEVER try to make ropes from sheets or blankets.
  If you are trapped in your room:
- Remain calm. Do not panic. Wait for help, since the fire department will give you instructions.
- Fill the tub with cold water. Stuff wet towels or cloths under the door, and use the masking tape to tape the top and sides of the door to keep out smoke and fumes.
- If smoke fills the room, hold a wet towel to your face. Stay low, close to the floor and as near to a window as possible.
- Know where you are, using the pen flashlight if necessary. Remember, even in familiar surroundings it is easy to become disoriented in a dark room filled with smoke.

Tips for Burn Victims

It is absolutely essential that burns get immediate, almost reflex attention. Even a minor burn can cause scarring, with more severe burns leading to shock trauma, infection, and death.

If clothing catches fire, many people try to run away from it or wave their arms or legs as if they were trying to shake out a match. Instead, they succeed only in fanning the flames. Remember, fires need oxygen to burn. The absolute rule when clothing catches fire is *STOP, DROP,* and *ROLL*. Stop wherever you are, drop to the floor, and roll over and over to smother the flames. (If readily accessible, you might grab a coat or blanket and roll another person in it to prevent igniting your own clothing.)

Cool a burn. Put cool water or ice on burned skin immediately. (Do not put grease or ointment on a burn, since it will seal the skin and prevent air from getting to the wound.) If the skin blisters or is blackened, seek immediate medical attention.

Gas Leaks

Natural gas is a popular fuel for heating, cooking, and operating certain appliances because it is clean, efficient, and, normally, trouble-free. However, if natural gas is allowed to escape into the atmosphere, there is an immediate danger of fire, explosion, or asphyxiation. For this reason, natural gas, which normally is odorless, is given an odor—so your nose knows that there is a leak. The gas will smell most strongly near the leak. However, if you smell gas, *act fast*—before trying to discover where it's coming from.

First, open all the windows. Then check to see that all the gas taps are turned off. The next step is to turn off the gas at the main, which normally is next to your meter on the inlet pipe. Using a wrench, give the shutoff valve a quarter turn in either direction so that it runs crosswise on the pipe. Then call the gas company immediately.

Even after determining where the gas odor is strongest, you may not be able to pinpoint the leak. You may wish to try applying warm, sudsy water in the general area of the leak. Escaping gas will cause the soapy water to bubble up. Under no circumstances should you try to locate the leak with a flame or electrical appliance, or turn light switches off or on if there is any suspicion of gas in the air. And once the gas is off, let the gas company turn it back on.

Should a gas main break in your neighborhood, evacuate the area immediately and notify both the fire department and the gas company as soon as you can get to a telephone.

Playing with gas is playing with fire and should be left to the fire fighters and gas companies. They know "hows," "whys," and "wherefores" of dealing with and correcting escaping gas problems *safely*.

Blackouts

In November 1965, all of New York City and much of the
Eastern Seaboard was plunged into darkness, with millions
stranded in elevators and buildings, with traffic snarled to a
standstill due to the lack of operating traffic lights. Although
this was a freak accident, there have been several major power
failures since. And while you're not likely to experience many
blackouts of such magnitude, you are quite likely to experience
power failures that frequently accompany strong storms,
floods, earthquakes, and other natural disasters. Furthermore,
many blackouts are "manmade"—caused by severe drains on
the power supply. This often happens on hot summer after-
noons and usually during "peak load" periods when air conditioners and other electrically powered apparatuses overload
the system.

Preventing Preventable Blackouts

"Manmade" blackouts are best prevented by energy conser-
vation procedures. Any equipment that produces light, heat, or
cooling uses the most energy. To prevent overloading the system and, therefore, blackouts, the following steps are recommended:
- Turn your air conditioner to its lowest setting and, if possible, turn it off and use a fan.
- Turn your refrigerator down to its warmest setting.

- Refrain from using electric lights, and shut off lights when
  you leave a room. Replace bulbs in your light fixtures with
  those having lower wattage.
- Refer to Chapter 4 for tips on handling power failures in cold
  or hot weather.

Preparing for a Predictable Power Failure

Although there are occasions when there is no advance
warning of a power failure, often you may be forewarned of
imminent storms and other natural disasters that may cause a
power failure. In both cases, be prepared by having the necessary equipment on hand and readily accessible. Among the
items highly recommended are:
- Emergency lighting: Keep a flashlight with fresh batteries in
  a place where you can easily find it. Candles are not recommended, especially in homes where there are children,
  because of the high risk of fire and also burns from candle
  wax.

- Radio: Make sure you have a transister radio with fresh batteries available to learn the scope of the problem, as well as the location of downed wires and other hazards.

- Cooking equipment: A camp stove or barbeque can offer an alternative method of food preparation during the blackout. However, remember not to use charcoal inside the house due to the hazards of toxic fumes.
- Shelf foods: It is better to have a supply of shelf foods such as crackers or peanut butter in stock than to have to use an alternative method of cooking.

- Generators: Some individuals may need standby equipment to provide electricity to power medical equipment, aquariums, and other devices that cannot be turned off. Moderately priced generators are now available for private homes, and you might want to inquire about the use of emergency generators in your high-rise apartment building.
- Surge protectors: These are recommended to protect particularly expensive electronic equipment, such as VCRs, televisions, computers, and the like.

What to Do in a Blackout

Although blackouts do not pose any real, direct threat to safety, it is easy to become disoriented if everything suddenly goes dark. Therefore, your first course of action is to take stock of where you are—don't move until your eyes become adjusted to the dark in order to prevent a dangerous fall.

If the blackout obviously is affecting your whole general area and appears that it's going to last a long time:

- Refrain from opening refrigerators or freezers: If the door remains shut, food should last approximately two days. In hot weather, you should also cover your refrigerator or freezer with a blanket to provide additional insulation.

- Refrain from using the phone: Although the phone will still work, phone use should be restricted to urgent calls.
- Turn off or unplug electrical apparatuses: Often when the electricity comes back on, there is a power surge. If you do not have surge protectors, this can damage or destroy some electrical appliances or televisions. Wait for a half hour after power has been restored before turning electrical and electronic equipment back on in order to give the system a chance to stabilize.

- If any cooking is done inside the home, do not use a barbe-cue or charcoal. A campstove may be safely used if the room is adequately ventilated and if the campstove is placed in a safe area where there won't be a fire risk.
- If there is a true emergency requiring electricity, such as running respirators or other life-support equipment, call the fire department and ask for an emergency generator.
- If there is a blackout while you are away from home, resist the temptation to head home immediately, since traffic lights and gas pumps will not operate without electricity.
- If stuck in an elevator, stay calm and periodically press the alarm button. It may be ringing somewhere even if you can't hear it. Unless you can hear rescuers, yelling is usually fruitless.

- Since downed electrical lines sometimes occur in a blackout situation, you should stay well away from them, and do NOT touch any object in contact with them. ANY downed line should be treated as if it were live. Utmost caution should be used in attempting to rescue anyone in contact with or near a downed or broken line. This is best attempted by the experts—fire fighters or electric company personnel.
- If attempting the rescue yourself, DO NOT touch the victim, since the electricity will be passed directly to you. Before trying to move the victim, stand on a dry object (a board or a rubber floor mat from your auto). Push the wire away with a dry board or stick to free the victim. DO NOT touch the wire with any object that is wet or is made of a metallic substance.

Chapter 3
Floods, Thunderstorms, and Lightning

Floods

Will you be among the hundreds of thousands of Americans who are driven from their homes by floodwaters each year? Disasters can strike anytime, anyplace, anyone. Part of the impact is frequently a great sense of helplessness, but it doesn't have to be that way. Although we can't prevent natural disasters, knowing what to do before they occur can make that vast difference for your family in survival—and successful coping.

Take floods, for example. No area is immune. A peaceful stream or river that we take for granted changes dramatically when extended rainfall or melting snows cause slow-rising waters to spill over its banks, or a hillside runoff suddenly cascades into a turbulent flash flood and heads for your home or vacation site. What would you do?

How to Prepare for Possible Floods

Begin by knowing the water level that is considered flood stage in your area and the elevation of your property in relation to waterways by checking with your department of public works. By doing this when you first move in, you can have a type of benchmark if the water-weather forecasts sound threatening.

Think in advance about how you and your family would deal with an emergency, how much extra assistance would be required for anyone who might be elderly or handicapped if you had to evacuate . . . and where you might go to be safe. Think what route you could take to get there (and a safe alternate, in case there might be flooding in that direction). Make sure every member of the family is aware of this in case you become separated.

While family safety is the prime consideration, there also are steps you can take beforehand to improve emergency living conditions and lessen property damage. It's good to keep on hand materials such as sandbags, plywood, plastic sheeting, lumber, and shovels. Be sure you know how to use these materials properly. For example, in flood conditions, sandbags should not be stacked *against* walls but rather somewhat *away* from them to avoid damaging the very property you are trying to protect. Local building contractors or the Office of Emergency Services can also give advice.

If you can, install check valves in building sewer traps to prevent floodwaters from backing up in sewer drains. Without check valves, have large corks or stoppers on hand to plug showers, tubs, or basins.

Since electric power may be interrupted, keep a stock of food that requires little cooking and no refrigeration. If the flood stage is such that you are forced to leave your home, it is a good idea, time allowing, to disconnect all electrical appliances while they are still dry before you leave, make sure all gas appliances are turned off, and shut off valves at storage tanks. Two other things to consider: Keep automobiles fueled in preparation for evacuation, and have self-contained power supplies available. All these lights, flashlights, emergency cooking equipment, and a portable radio should be user-ready at all times, with their batteries in good working order.

Consider what might happen if a flood would force you to leave your property. Before it actually reaches the threatening stage, the family could move essential items to upper floors or safe ground, see that fuel and storage tanks are filled to keep them from floating away, and grease immovable machinery. Pack a bag with the kind of essentials that may be difficult for you or others to remember to gather up in an emergency: medications, eyeglasses, any special diet foods, proper clothing, and important papers you might need.

Human lives and safety are the first priority, but if there should be time before you are forced to evacuate, don't forget to shut off the water main to isolate contaminated water from your water heater. By doing this, you could protect something that could provide a source of emergency drinking water when you are able to return. Bring inside, or securely tie down any outdoor possessions that could be hurled about or swept away by the swirling floodwaters. If you have any penned livestock, leave those gates open so they, too, can move to safer places.

Keep Alert

Stay aware of heavy rains and how road conditions are affected. Monitor what you currently face or something that sounds as though it seems to be developing rapidly. Be sure you are tuned in to hear any advance warnings. The National Oceanic and Atmospheric Administration (NOAA) makes this information available on weather radio (162.400/162.550 mhz) and to area radio and TV stations. Radios are available that carry only this information.

The forecasts of impending floods will indicate which bodies of water are affected, when and where the flooding is likely to begin, and whether this flooding may be mild, moderate, or severe. Also the National Weather Service and public safety agencies will have reports on flooding in process. If you aren't where broadcast information is available, watch out for indicators of flash flooding, such as a rapid rise in the river level or an increase in the speed of stream flow.

Campers especially may not hear these broadcast warnings and should pay particular attention to potential danger. One thing to avoid is camping on low ground, because flash floods could hit while campers are sleeping. Even if you're not at the bottom of the hill, it is still possible to be a target. Use of maps not only will show campers where they are, but also can point the way to higher ground when the move for safety is necessary.

Sometimes people become confused about the terms "flood watch" and "flood warning." In general, a FLOOD WATCH (for weather-related conditions) means conditions are such that emergencies *may* occur. A FLOOD WARNING means that the event either is actually occurring or has a very strong probability of occurring. Therefore, a flood watch indicates the possibility of flooding occurring in specific areas. In this case you should *be alert* for the flooding conditions that may develop. Don't leave your home unless the flooding is heading your way or the authorities order you to leave.

However, if you hear the words FLOOD WARNING, it means flooding is occurring or is imminent in the general area where you are. Be prepared to respond quickly.

Reaching Higher Ground

Before you leave, if time allows, make sure that a friend or relative knows where you are planning to go (for example, to the home of a friend, relative, or a Red Cross shelter), by which route, and when you estimate you will be able to arrive.

Once you and your family are on the road, watch for flooding at highway dips, bridges, and low areas, and be aware of signs such as thunder or lightning, which could signify a distant storm bringing even more heavy rainfall to the vicinity.

Be careful to stay out of any areas you know are subject to sudden flooding, especially at night, when it isn't easy to see potential danger signs. Do not drive over flooded roads. You can't tell whether part of the road or a bridge may be washed out, how deep the water is, or how quickly the water level will rise. Cars can float dangerously under these conditions before they are swept downstream.

If your car stalls, abandon the car immediately and get all members of your family out at the same time, before the water can get any deeper. Don't let the children dawdle by the flood-waters. Move everyone quickly to higher ground. There have been too many cases where rapidly rising waters have swept vehicle and occupants away.

After the Flood

Flood dangers don't end when the waters begin to recede. That's why, if you had to evacuate, you should not return home until the authorities say it is safe. Even then, you must be aware of hazards you may face. The main ones are gas leaks, electrical hazards, structural damage, and unsafe drinking water. Therefore, it is sound procedure to have the place checked by a reputable building contractor, or other specialist such as a plumber or electrician, before you reenter your home.

BE CAREFUL. Have an authority check for structural damage and danger of collapse *before* you enter your place. If it is okay and you are able to go inside to examine your home, use a flashlight, not a lantern or torch. Watch out for falling debris and dangerous damage that may have been done to floors and walls. *Check for gas leaks*. Make sure there aren't any. Sometimes your own nose can tell you if there is the smell of gas from a leak. If so, lose no time in getting to a usable telephone to ask the gas company for help.

 BE CAREFUL OF THE POSSIBILITIES OF ELECTRO-CUTION. Make sure you're wearing rubber-soled shoes and rubber gloves and that the power company knows about any broken utility lines. Don't turn on any lights or use *any* flooded electrical appliances until they have been reconditioned. When you're checking electrical circuits, do so *only* if the electricity is turned off. Also, when the power has been off for a period of time, any food that was left in the refrigerator or freezer is likely to be spoiled. Don't take chances by trying to use it.

DON'T DRINK THE WATER UNTIL YOU'RE SURE. Never walk in after a flood and think it's okay to turn on a faucet and drink the water *unless* the health department has announced that it is safe to do so. To avoid contaminated drinking water, you can boil water for ten minutes in a clean container as an emergency measure.

DRYING OUT. Even though you're anxious to remove water from your home, do not rush it. If the basement is completely flooded, pump about a third of the water out each day, since too drastic a change in pressure could cause the walls to cave in. Shovel out mud while it is still moist to give walls and floors a chance to dry.

RECOUPING YOUR LOSSES. If your community is participating in the National Flood Insurance Program and you have this insurance, call your agent or broker to arrange the assignment of an adjuster to inspect your property. Also take pictures of the flood damage, and save all receipts for temporary repairs.

Thunderstorms and Lightning

A severe thunderstorm has a number of troublemakers: heavy rains, which can cause flash flooding; strong winds; and lightning. And any one of these aspects has the potential for a dangerous situation.

Although thunderstorms occasionally happen in the winter, prime time is a hot, sultry day when dark, heavy clouds begin to form and you notice that the temperature has dropped suddenly with an increase in gusty winds. Your best protection is to get inside, taking shelter in a sturdy building. Turn on your battery-operated radio in case there is news of a tornado watch, but generally the major danger will come from lightning, an electrical discharge that results from the buildup of static electricity between clouds and the ground. While present in all thunderstorms, it is more noticeable when the storm is severe.

"Killer" Lightning

Lightning kills or injures more people than any other natural hazard in this country. While most of the victims survive, lightning still kills more people than floods, hurricanes, or tornadoes. Lightning also can knock down trees and trigger fires. A way to estimate the distance between you and a lightning strike is to count the seconds that elapse between the flash and the thunderclap. If the count is less than five seconds, don't lose time—take shelter and stay inside while there is lightning activity. Don't go back outside unless it is *absolutely* necessary.

There are other precautions to take. Do not handle any kind of electrical equipment or telephones during an electrical storm, because lightning could follow the wire. Stay away from TV sets, because they are dangerous at this time. Close all windows and doors, then stay away from them, too. Also things such as a water faucet, a sink, or a tub with metal pipes could conduct electricity and should be avoided.

Don't Attract Lightning by Being the Tallest Object Around

It's dangerous to be the tallest object in an open area. Get as far as you can from hilltops and trees, particularly any tree that stands alone. If you are caught outdoors, try to seek shelter in a building (but NOT a small, isolated shed or any other small structure that is in an open area), cave, or depression in the ground, and keep away from fences, telephone lines, or power lines. If you feel an electrical charge such as having your hair stand on end or feel that your skin tingles, it means that lightning may be about to strike you, so drop to the ground immediately. Just make sure not to lie flat, since the wet ground can carry electricity—it's better to kneel with your feet close together and your head lowered.

If you are using metal equipment such as tractors, golf carts, motorcycles, lawnmowers, shovels, bicycles, or even hanging clothes on a metal line, get away from things that can be electrical conductors. If you are on a farm, try to get the livestock to shelter because they won't know how to take the precautions a human would.

Sometimes you may not have a choice about seeking shelter. If that happens, make sure you go to a low place. Even in the forest, look for a low area, and make your refuge under a thick growth of *small, not tall* trees. When outdoors in a storm, be alert to flash floods (see the section on floods) as well as lightning dangers. And don't ever think that just because lightning has struck a place *once*, it's safe. That's an old wives' tale about lightning never striking twice. It can, and has been known to, strike the same place—or the same person—several times.

Other than being in a building, about the best place to be in a severe thunderstorm is in a car. If inside, stay there until the storm passes, because the car will give excellent protection from lightning once you have pulled away from any trees that might fall on the vehicle. Going from best to worst, about the worst place you could be in a storm with a lot of lightning is on water. On flat, open water a small boat, or even a swimmer, is the highest object lightning can find there and is likely to be a target. At the *first sign* of a thunderstorm, lose no time in heading for shore.

If the worst should happen and someone you are with should be struck by lightning, the person will receive a strong electrical shock and possible burns, but you will not be in danger if you touch the victim and try to help. The lightning strike may cause the victim's heart and breathing to stop, so prompt use of cardiopulmonary resuscitation (CPR) can be used to revive the person. Treat any injuries or burns you can, but make sure the victim gets medical attention.

Heavy Rains

Frequently one of the results of a severe thunderstorm is a flash flood. Wherever you are, try to know beforehand about high ground and how to get there quickly in case you should see or hear rapidly rising water.

Hail—the Underrated Hazard

Although it rarely takes lives, hail can be terribly destructive to the crops we depend on for food. Hail precipitation is in the form of balls or clumps of ice. Hail can be as small as a pea or the size of a golf ball. Some are even larger—at 2³/₄ inches, they are as big as baseballs. The severe storms with intense updrafts are the most likely to produce the large hail.

In case of hailstorms, take shelter. Hail is potentially dangerous for pets and livestock, so be sure to take care of them as well.

In the Aftermath of the Thunderstorm

Once the storm is over and you are home, check for any possible damage. While you are doing so, be careful to avoid any downed electric power lines. Also, if the electricity is off, use your battery-operated radio to listen for any warnings of flash floods or tornadoes if they are threats in your area.

Chapter 4
Dangers from Winter and Heat

Winter Dangers

Bitter cold and winter storms can cause extremely serious hazards for the housebound as well as for those who must be outside. Being familiar with the meaning of the wording of weather news from the National Weather Service will let you be aware of advance notice to get in supplies or make alternative arrangements.

Winter storm watch means that severe winter weather conditions may affect your area. This can be freezing rain, sleet, or heavy snow happening in combination or separately.

The difference between *freezing rain* and *sleet* is that freezing rain freezes on impact, while sleet is composed of ice pellets that bounce when they hit the ground; but both can make driving hazardous. Freezing rain is called an ice storm when a substantial glaze layer accumulates, and in some parts of the country it is known as "silver thaws" or black ice. When the ice coating is heavy on exposed surfaces, falling trees or falling wires can be additional hazards.

Snow squalls are brief, intense snowfalls with gusty surface winds, while the words *heavy snow* indicate that four or more inches are likely to fall during a twelve-hour period, or six or more inches during a twenty-four-hour period.

The *blizzard* is the most dangerous of all the winter storms, combining cold air, heavy snow, and the kind of strong winds that blow the snow about and may reduce visibility to only a few yards. Although a blizzard warning may be issued when winds of at least thirty-five miles per hour and considerable falling and/or blowing snows are expected for several hours, this warning usually is associated with winds of fifty to sixty miles per hour as well as temperatures of twenty-five to thirty degrees Fahrenheit. In addition to the blizzard warning there may be a separate one for *high winds*. These are sustained winds of over forty miles per hour, or gusts of at least fifty miles per hour or more, expected to last for at least an hour. Severe blizzard warnings also indicate that temperatures of ten degrees Fahrenheit or lower and very heavy snowfalls are expected.

Ground blizzards are a combination of blowing and drifting snow after a snowfall.

An additional danger can be spotted with *cold wave* warnings about an expected rapid temperature drop of twenty degrees Fahrenheit or more during a twenty-four-hour period.

Wind-Chill Impact

The *wind-chill factor* combination of cold and wind can put a relatively balmy winter day in the throes of a cold wave. For example, a thirty-degree Fahrenheit day would feel like eleven degrees Fahrenheit if the winds were fifteen miles per hour, but it would feel like two degrees Fahrenheit *below* zero if thirty-mile-per-hour winds were blowing. Imagine what it's like when the weather really hits zero! Then those same wind speeds would make it the equivalent of minus thirty-three degrees Fahrenheit and minus forty-nine degrees Fahrenheit, respectively.

If you have to be working outdoors in cold weather when the winds are strong, take extra precautions, because the conditions make it easy to become exhausted more quickly and become more susceptible to frostbite—or even death. Stockmen should remember that livestock are affected by this, too.

Be Sure You Know How to Protect Yourself and Your Family

If you haven't the necessary items on hand (battery-powered equipment, heating fuel, food and other supplies, a winter-ready car) by the time you have heard the storm warnings, get them immediately.

Since winter transportation becomes more difficult, keep your car in top operating condition and the gasoline tank as nearly full as possible. Also carry a "winter storm car kit" with you, which would contain: sleeping bags or two or more blankets (newspapers can substitute, as they can provide layers of insulation); winter clothing, which includes wool caps, mittens, and overshoes; matches and candles; a large box of facial tissues; a first-aid kit; flashlight with extra batteries; a small sack of sand; a set of tire chains; a shovel; a waterproof container filled with food supplies that are high-calorie and nonperishable, such as canned nuts, dried fruits, and candy; tools—pliers, a screwdriver, and an adjustable wrench; a windshield scraper; a transistor radio with extra batteries; and a set of battery booster cables.

Even with your car preparations, take public transportation if you can, driving only if it is necessary *and with all possible caution*. Try to travel by daylight, using major highways and roads, keeping the radio turned on for weather information, and in convoy with another vehicle, if possible. Also make sure, as with floods and any other disaster condition, that your route *and an alternate* have been planned ahead . . . and that someone else knows these plans.

If the conditions on the road become impossible, seek refuge immediately, but don't panic if there's no house close at hand and your car breaks down. In that case make sure your car shows a trouble signal, then get inside the car and *stay there* until help arrives. Avoid overexertion and exposure, but keep a downwind window slightly open for fresh air. Be careful it doesn't become sealed with snow or freezing rain. *Beware of carbon monoxide*. Run the heater sparingly (only when the downwind window is open), and keep the exhaust pipe clear. As much as you can in the car, try to exercise from time to time. If someone is with you, take turns keeping watch. Also be sure to turn on the dome light at night.

A Safe Return

Once you're safely in your dwelling, you and your family have to be prepared for isolation at home. Even in urban places, you may not be able to get out for a day or so, and in rural areas one should plan on how it would be possible to survive *if stranded for a week or two*.

DRESS WARMLY. Wear multiple layers of protective clothing, hoods, scarves, mittens, or gloves. If you have to go outside, cover your mouth to protect the lungs from the extremely cold air.

AVOID OVEREXERTION. Cold weather, without any physical exertion, puts an extra strain on the heart. When unaccustomed exercise is added, such as shoveling snow, pushing a car, or even walking long distances or very rapidly, there is the risk of a heart attack, a stroke, or even death. Don't push your body too far—it's too dangerous a risk to take.

WHEN THE POWER FAILS. With weather conditions like this, power failures are likely to occur. When this happens, keeping warm is a major problem, but there are many other things to consider as well to maintain a reasonable degree of comfort and to protect property.

FREEZING PIPES. If it seems likely that the heat will be off for at least several hours, try to protect exposed plumbing by draining all pipes, including hot water heating pipes in any rooms where the temperature falls below forty degrees Fahrenheit. Drain the sink, tub, and shower traps, toilet tanks and bowls, hot water heater, dish and clothes washers, water pumps, and furnace boiler. Try to save as much water as possible when draining the system, since a power outage could knock out your electrically powered water pump and restrict water use. This water should be stored in closed or covered containers, if possible in a place where it won't freeze. While heating system water is unfit for drinking or other household use, in case of emergency you could use the water from your hot-water heater and toilet tank (not bowl) for these purposes, since a power outage could knock out an electrically powered water pump.

COOKING. Meal-in-a-can foods such as stews, soups, canned meats, beans, or spaghetti require little heat for cooking, and while not a first choice, many can be eaten without any cooking. Also good to keep on hand: cereals, breads, dried meats, and cheese, and the kind of freeze-dried meals used by campers and backpackers. If you have a fireplace or a cooking camp stove, it is a good backup for emergency use. Be sure to use these only in a well-ventilated area.

 SANITATION. If the water supply is cut off, a portable camper's toilet might be useful. Otherwise, flush the toilet only often enough to prevent clogging. The chain or lever attached to the toilet handle can be disconnected to prevent children from overflushing. Provide covered containers for the disposal of toilet paper.

 HEATING AND LIGHTING. Since it may not be possible for regular heating supplies to be delivered, use the fuel you have sparingly. If need be, close off the rooms where heat is not essential. Make sure you have a backup kind of emergency heating equipment and fuel, such as a camp stove in case you don't have a fireplace. Also when the electricity is off you'll want to make sure that kerosene or gas lanterns are available and that ample fuel is on hand.

 An important backup is a dependable flashlight with spare bulbs and batteries. Remember, it is crucial to have proper ventilation and to know how to use emergency heating and lighting equipment to prevent fires or dangerous fumes. Watch out for burning charcoal in particular, as it can give off deadly amounts of carbon monoxide.

Be sure every member of the family knows the precautions, but also keep on hand tools and equipment that could be used to fight a fire if such should happen, because it would be *very difficult* to obtain fire department help in such weather conditions.

KEEPING IN TOUCH WITH THE OUTER WORLD. Even without your electric power, a battery-powered radio will make it possible to hear weather forecasts, information, and advice from local authorities. Be sure to keep extra batteries on hand so your radio won't fade out and be useless.

Protecting the Elderly

Even without storm conditions, winter cold is particularly hard on the elderly, who are more susceptible to hypothermia, the state when the body temperature is lowered. A body temperature below ninety-five degrees Fahrenheit is considered dangerous. Some of the other symptoms to watch for are pale skin and a bloated face, a trembling that is present on one side of the body, or in the arm or leg; slurred speech; an irregular and slowed heartbeat; and unusual drowsiness, perhaps lapsing into a coma. To prevent hypothermia, see that you, if you are elderly, or your elderly relative or neighbor takes certain precautions. Hot meals and hot liquids help, as does eating plenty of fruits and vegetables and adequate amounts of protein. Alcoholic beverages should be avoided because they cause the body to lose heat at a faster rate.

Notice what your elderly relative or friend is wearing. Warm, loose-fitting clothes are good indoors or out. However, when the elderly brave the outside, they should wear hats (you lose heat faster from your head than from any other part of your body) that cover their ears and have a warm scarf around the neck. Mittens will hold hand warmth better than gloves. Tight-fitting shoes and overshoes are not good.

Body heat can be increased by a daily exercise routine, no matter how simple. However, overexertion should be avoided at all costs because it strains the heart.

Since a number of the elderly don't get outside all that often in the winter, make sure their indoor room temperature is kept at a comfortable level. Caulking doors and windows plus closing draperies and shades at night will help keep the heat in, as will placing a rug at the bottom of doors to reduce drafts.

Encourage piling on plenty of blankets at bedtime, not to mention wearing a nightcap and socks to bed.

IF LIVING ALONE AS AN ELDERLY PERSON YOURSELF. The most important thing here is to remember to *keep in touch*. Have your nearby family member, a friend, or a neighbor check on you daily with a phone call or a visit. Make sure the numbers you need—of these people and of other key "help" in your life, such as your doctor and emergency ambulance service—are posted prominently, where the list will be close at hand if needed. If you are a relative or friend to someone elderly, see that someone checks up on them on a regular basis to make sure of their well-being.

More Cold-Weather Tips

ICE SKATING SAFETY. Ice skating is great fun, but there are certain precautions to take, and the first involves the condition of the lake or pond.

Don't skate if:
• The ice is clouded with air bubbles or other discolorations.
• There is moving water under the surface, or ice near springs or streams.
• Partially submerged objects can be seen, such as tree stumps, drainage pipes, or rocks.
• Thin ice is near the shore.
• Ice-fishing holes have become manmade hazards.

- It's difficult to see the ice too well because of strong sunlight hitting the ice and reflecting off sand or gravel.
  If you should fall through the ice:
- Don't panic. Send someone for help, then give yourself a moment to gain more stability. By kicking your feet up behind you, you keep your legs from jackknifing, and you can float.
- Try to swim from the breakthrough onto the ice. When you get there, roll or crawl on your stomach until you have gotten a safe distance from the hole.
- As soon as you're back on shore, get to a place where you can wrap up in warm blankets and drink hot liquids. Also see a doctor to make sure you prevent frostbite or hypothermia.
  How you can help if you see someone else fall through the ice:
- Extend something like a rope, tree limb, or broom to the person. Then slide gently toward the one in the water, extending the object and calling encouragement. However, if you notice any signs or sounds of ice cracking where you are, crawl back fast.
- Once you have the person on shore, being in a warm car will enhance the effects of giving the victim hot drinks and wrapping in warm blankets. See that the feet are elevated, and get the person to a doctor immediately.

Cold-Weather Survival

To protect plumbing, sewage systems, and appliances to prevent damage from freezing during winter power failures or other heating emergencies:

Hot-Water Systems

Keep exposed heating pipes from freezing by circulating water through the pipes or adding antifreeze to the system.

1. *Circulating water.* If electrical power is available, keep the circulator pump going, as moving water does not freeze readily. However, if room temperature drops below forty degrees Fahrenheit you probably should begin to drain the pipes, which isn't always so easy.
2. *Draining pipes.* Pipes may have to be disconnected to drain low points in the hot-water heating system. Open the vents on the radiators to release the air so the pipes can drain.

3. *Adding antifreeze.* Consult a heating contractor before you add antifreeze to your system because antifreeze is poisonous and mustn't be allowed to get into the drinking-water system. Use *only* antifreeze containing ethylene glycol, and make sure that the house water system and the boiler water system are not connected. Be careful *not* to use any antifreeze that contains methanol, which vaporizes readily when heated and could cause excessive pressure in the system. It is important, too, that the antifreeze you select does not contain any leak-stopping additives, because they might foul the pumps, valves, air vents, and other parts.

Plumbing System
1. Shut off the water at the main valve, or turn off the well pump if it is in the house.
2. Drain the pressure tank.
3. Open all the faucets until they are completely drained. Since some valves will open only when there is water pressure, it will be necessary in that case to remove the valve from the faucet.
4. Drain the entire system by disconnecting pipe unions or joints as close to the main valve as possible. You may use compressed air to blow water from pipes.
5. Insulate undrainable pipes around their main valves. Use newspaper, blankets, or housing insulation for this purpose.
6. Drain toilet flush tanks and spray hoses.
7. Disconnect the water softening unit so water can drain from the hard- and soft-water pipes and from the controls. Lay the softener tank on its side to drain as much water as possible. Also drain controls and tubing on brine (salt) tanks. A brine tank itself will not be harmed by freezing.

Sewage System

1. Empty all drain traps by carefully removing drain plugs or by disconnecting traps.
2. Blow out inaccessible traps with compressed air, or add ethylene-glycol-base antifreeze in an amount equal to the water in the trap (one pint to one quart is sufficient, depending on the size of the trap).
3. Check kitchen sinks, bathroom sinks, bathtub drains, toilets, washtubs, showers, floor drains, and sump pumps.

Appliances

1. Disconnect the electric power or shut off the fuel to all water-using units.
2. Shut off the water supply and disconnect the hoses, if possible.
3. Drain all water-using appliances.
4. Check the water heater, humidifier, ice-making unit of the refrigerator, washing machine, and dishwasher. Drain the pumps on the washing machine and the dishwasher. Do NOT put antifreeze in these appliances. Close valves to the furnace, water heater, and dryer.

Dangers from Heat

Although many people look forward to summer and being outdoors, excess heat and overexposure to the sun have cruel effects, causing heat-related illnesses.

Some serious signs of heat illnesses are dizziness, rapid heartbeat, diarrhea, nausea, throbbing headache, dry skin (no sweating), chest pain, great weakness, mental changes, breathing problems, vomiting, and cramps.

If you, or someone you know, experiences these symptoms, *call for help*. In hot weather as well as in cold, it is important to stay in contact with others for mutual support and well-being. If you, a relative, or a friend lives alone, be sure the individual makes special efforts to maintain daily telephone contact with the people who know the person.

Types of Heat-Related Illnesses

Usually the body's thermostat will cause sweating if a person becomes heated from working, playing, or just being in a hot area. However, if that temperature control system stops working correctly, the body doesn't cool as it would ordinarily, and overexposure to the heat and sun can result in a heat stroke. High body temperature in connection with this is also caused by overexertion or strenuous physical activity in hot temperatures, and the kind and amount of clothing worn.

Symptoms to watch for are a body temperature that may be 106 degrees Fahrenheit or even higher, the skin being hot, red, and dry, and a rapid, strong pulse. The victim may be unconscious. If this occurs, *immediately* place the victim in a tub of cold water (do not add ice), or sponge the skin repeatedly with cool water or rubbing alcohol. If fans or air conditioners are available, use them. Once the victim's temperature goes below

102 degrees Fahrenheit, take care to prevent overchilling, and see that the victim is NOT given stimulants. Be sure to seek medical help *as soon as possible*.

A heat exhaustion victim's body temperature is different from that of a heat stroke victim. The person suffering from heat exhaustion will have a body temperature that is normal, or nearly normal. Here there is excessive pooling of blood in the capillaries of the skin as the body struggles to lose heat. This pooling interferes with the circulation of the blood to vital organs such as the brain, heart, and lungs. While the body is trying to compensate for this reduced supply of blood not being where it is needed in the critical areas, the smaller veins constrict. The skin becomes white or pale and cool and clammy. The victim may faint but probably will regain consciousness if the head is lowered so that the blood supply to the brain can be improved.

Symptoms of heat exhaustion are weakness, nausea, and dizziness. Cramping also is possible.

As soon as you are aware of the condition, give the victim sips of salt water (one teaspoonful of salt per glass) but *slowly*, half a glass every fifteen minutes, over a period of about an hour. Loosen the victim's clothes and have the person lie down with feet raised from eight to twelve inches. Apply wet, cool cloths and fan the person, or move to an air-conditioned room. If the victim should vomit, don't give any more fluids, but take the person to the hospital, where intravenous salt solution can be given.

After an attack like this, the heat exhaustion victim should be advised not to return to work for several days and be particularly careful to be protected from exposure to abnormally warm temperatures.

While heat cramps caused by inadequate intake of water and salt and overexposure to the heat and sun are not as serious as heat exhaustion and heat strokes, they, too, should be treated carefully.

The symptoms are cramping of the victim's leg and abdominal muscles. For this condition, as with heat exhaustion, sips of salt water prove helpful. Give the victim about half a glass (with one teaspoonful of salt per glass) every fifteen minutes, over a period of about an hour. Also a good way to give first aid is to exert pressure with your hands on the cramped muscles or gently massage them to relieve the discomfort of the spasms.

Caring for the Elderly

Since older persons are less likely to sweat or have widening of blood vessels to transfer heat from the body core to the skin, these body mechanisms function less effectively. This leads them to suffer more when the thermometer hits ninety degrees Fahrenheit or above and when the humidity also soars. This temperature/humidity combination can cause heat in the body to build, interfering with its proper function.

High-risk elderly are those who have chronic conditions that affect the body's heat-regulating capacity. These conditions include diabetes, heart disease, arteriosclerosis, high blood pressure, Parkinson's disease, and stroke. Other risk conditions include overweight, burns or skin disease, conditions that reduce the capacity to sweat, alcoholism, and diarrhea.

If not in air-conditioned surroundings, these people should make it a point to drink at least a gallon of liquid any day the temperature goes over ninety-five degrees Fahrenheit. And the overweight or someone who exercises a great deal would need to drink *even more* than that for protection. When it comes to food, a well-balanced diet is wise as always, but keep the emphasis on meals that seem light and cool, NOT hot and heavy.

How Anyone Can Help to Beat a Heat Wave

Sometimes a heat wave catches us unawares even if it is summer, but we try to keep going at our usual pace. *Take it easy.* Be gentle to yourself and allow your body to get acclimated to the environment for the first two or three hot days.

The National Oceanic and Atmospheric Administration has a number of tips they recommend. The first is to listen when your body warns you that the heat is too high. When this happens, slow down. Reduce your level of activity immediately, and get into a cooler environment if you can.

Lightweight and light-colored clothing makes good summer sense, as does light eating. Foods such as protein increase your metabolic heat production and water loss. Also, unless you are on a salt-restricted diet, make sure you and your family include salt in the diet. And drink *plenty* of water.

Watch out for too much sunshine. It's very easy to get a burn even if you're not at the beach, and sunburn inhibits the body's ability to cool itself. Even if you HAVE to be outside, make a point of trying to get out of the heat for at least a few hours each day.

Making Air Conditioning More Effective

Because an air conditioner cools and dehumidifies air, setting the fan speed on high will cool more effectively. However, if the weather is humid, set the fan speed on *low*. While the lower speed may not cool as effectively as the high, it does a better job of dehumidifying, so it will add to the room's comfort index. Another thing to remember is that the place is NOT going to cool down faster if you just turn the thermostat down. Air conditioners will run longer to reach this lower temperature setting, and cost more to run due to the wasted electricity.

Air conditioner filters should be vacuumed weekly during periods of heavy usage, and replaced if they look worn.

For window air conditioners, close any floor heat registers nearby because cool air falls, and this cool air will spill through any of these openings. A snug fit between air conditioner and window opening can be made even snugger by insulating any spaces here. You also can increase the effectiveness of the window air conditioner by using a circulating or box fan to spread cool air.

If you want your storm windows to do double duty, don't take them down when the first warm days of spring arrive. They're great for adding better insulation all summer long. Just make sure you check your air-conditioning ducts for proper insulation.

What to Do With *or Without* an Air Conditioner

Don't use any heat-producing appliance that will make indoor temperatures even hotter during the sizzling part of the day. This can include ovens, clothes dryers, dishwashers, toasters, and electric lights. If you have to cook or are taking a shower (and try to make it a cool one if there is no medical problem), avoid extreme temperature changes; this may cause hypothermia in some, particularly the elderly and the very young. It's okay to switch on the exhaust fan, but make sure to turn it off when you are through to keep it from pulling any cool air out.

Plan cool meals that don't require cooking, but if you have to cook indoors, do it in the early morning or late evening. Cook outdoors if you can. As part of the summer diet, make sure everyone in the family drinks plenty of nonalcoholic fluids. This will help avoid the dehydration caused by excessive perspiration.

Slow down; avoid excessive activity. By staying in north-facing rooms when you can late in the day, you'll be as far from the sun's direct rays as possible. As mentioned earlier, clothes should be light in color, light in texture, and loose in fit.

Some closing down helps the cooling-off process. If you must do a heat-producing job, by closing off this area from the rest of the house until you finish (if you can stand the extra heat when no ventilation system exists in the space), it helps avoid heat buildup in the other rooms. Whether you live in an apartment or a house, placing temporary reflectors (such as aluminum foil-covered cardboard) snugly against the window can reflect the heat back outside. This is an easy-to-make project that the younger members of the family may want to tackle. Another way to keep the inside cool air from oozing out is to weatherstrip doors and windowsills.

If you are lucky enough to have big shade trees outside, that will help insulate the windows from the sun and outside heat. However, shades, draperies, awnings, or louvers are more effective for those windows that get the morning or evening sun. If you're able to use outdoor awnings or louvers, you'll find they are the most effective ways to reduce heat (estimated as a solar gain cut of 80 percent). People who have houses also might want to consider an after-sundown water spraying of brick or masonry walls. While this may just cool the structure by a few degrees, it will lessen radiation of stored heat into the living area.

Dust Storms

Extremely dry and hot weather may result in dust storms. When the weather seems threatening, be sure to listen for warnings about possible dust storms. This warning means bad news for drivers: visibility of one-half mile or less due to the blowing dust (or sand), and wind speeds of thirty miles per hour or more.

Although such storms may last only a few minutes, they strike with little warning. Suddenly an advancing wall of dust and debris appears, and it is no small wall. It may be miles long and several thousand feet high. The dust blinds and chokes as it quickly reduces visibility. The accidents it can cause may involve chain collisions and massive pileups.

By taking certain actions you, as a motorist, can save your own and other lives. If it is too late to avoid entering the dust storm area, take these actions:

Pull your vehicle off the pavement as far as possible as soon as you see dense dust approaching or blowing across the roadway. Stop, *turn off the lights*, set the emergency brake, and *take your foot off of the brake pedal* to make sure that the tail lights are not illuminated.

The reason for making sure that *all* lights are off is that when vehicles leave the road and keep the lights on, other vehicles approaching from the rear sometimes use the advance car's light as a guide. When this happens, the second car inadvertently goes off the road—and in some instances has actually collided with the parked vehicle.

If you can't pull off the road, proceed at a speed that is suitable for visibility. In this case, *turn on* the lights and sound the horn occasionally. The painted center line can help guide you. *Never* stop on the traveled portion of the road—look for a safe place to pull off.

Chapter 5
Earthquakes, Hurricanes, and Tornadoes

Earthquakes

Earthquakes can strike areas far beyond the San Francisco area and the San Andreas Fault. While many associate California with earthquakes, the state with the largest number of major earthquakes is actually Alaska. Since earthquakes generally occur along cracks in the earth's crust known as faults, a number of our other western states have the potential for earthquakes, including Nevada, Hawaii, Montana, Oregon, Utah, and Washington. Sometimes "freak" earthquakes may occur elsewhere.

East of the Rocky Mountains, Missouri is the area of greatest hazard. It was the site of the devastating New Madrid earthquake, the largest historic earthquake to hit the continental United States. However, others have struck many other places as well—as far away as the St. Lawrence River valley and Charleston, South Carolina.

Since this violence strikes without warning, families should know what to do *before* it may happen, particularly in the earthquake-prone areas.

Specially hazardous are buildings with foundations resting on landfill, old waterways, or other soft and unstable soil. Also in the hazardous category are trailers or mobile homes, because they tend to become uncomfortably mobile when a quake is in progress.

Your "earthquake survival kit" should be kept at hand where it is readily available. Include in it these objects: hand-operated can opener, wrench, flashlight, battery-operated radio with extra batteries, first-aid kit, nonperishable foods, and a supply of water.

When a quake strikes, the major casualty problems are not caused by the actual earth movement. Rather they come from falling objects and debris such as flying glass from broken windows, fires from broken gas lines, fallen power lines, or from the landslides and huge ocean waves a quake may trigger. Another common cause of injuries is inappropriate action resulting from panic. There are a number of steps you can take beforehand to help your family know what to do so this is not as likely to occur.

BE PREPARED. Check your home for hazards, and hold family earthquake drills. To some members of the family "the earthquake game" might sound childish, but it is one of the best ways to recognize safety hazards that can be reduced or eliminated. It also helps individuals to improve their reaction time, since the game takes only a few minutes to play.

The Earthquake Game

Step 1. The game starts when any member of the group calls out "earthquake!" At that point everyone drops what he or she is doing and participates.

Step 2. Discuss what would happen in the room if it were a real earthquake. Do this in every room of the dwelling. For example, in a kitchen, cupboard doors would fly open and dishes and glassware would come crashing out. The refrigerator door would open, and things such as eggs would smash and the other refrigerator contents spill forth while the heavy refrigerator can slide all the way across the room and turn upside down. Other parts of the kitchen chaos might include falling fixtures and ceiling panels, while another room would be especially prone to shattering glass and the fall of heavy hanging objects.

Step 3. Once you have identified what might happen, discuss how you could avoid injury in each room. Generally this means coverage in the sense of getting under something or getting something over you. In the kitchen or dining room, this might mean a door frame. When you are under a table, hold on to it, as it may "creep" away from you.

In other rooms, it could mean holding pillows over the head, or crawling under a bed. THE IMPORTANT THING is to *do physically what you expect to do if an earthquake actually strikes.* When there is no obvious furniture to crawl under or

material to pull over yourself, assume a "duck and cover" position. Look for a corner, a door frame, or even an inside wall where you might lean for protection.

The benefits of playing this game include doing such things as thinking of how to secure cabinet doors and bolt down items such as refrigerators or water heaters; and realizing the importance of fastening topheavy furniture to the walls and also relocating beds away from large windows for greater protection. You also will save precious seconds in case of the real thing, and will know what to do instinctively when the ground or room begins to shake.

This is particularly important because most family members today arc in different places during the daytime. Even if separated from one another, this experience will help every member of the family to be better prepared for protection, because it is important for everyone that protection be found within a yard or two of where the person is when a quake starts. In a severe earthquake, it just isn't possible to move far—say, all the way across the room—because of the intensity of the ground shaking.

Make sure that large and heavy objects are placed on lower shelves and that the shelves are securely fastened to the walls. Any bottled goods or breakables should be stored in low or closed cabinets, and overhead lighting fixtures should be made fast. In new construction and alterations, earthquake-resistant building standards should be adhered to. Any sites for construction should be selected and engineered to reduce the dangers of possible earthquake damage.

Other things to do before the quake hits:

1. Teach responsible family members how to turn off utilities at the main switches and valves.
2. Take first-aid training, and have a fire extinguisher and first-aid kit available.
3. Keep immunizations and medications up to date, and gather together supplies and medications that would allow your family to survive for at least seventy-two hours. This includes food, water, and clothing.
4. Don't forget to maintain a flashlight and battery-powered radio in good shape in case power is cut off.

Also consider what might happen if you become separated. The plan for family reunification should be one known well by everyone.

While these measures have related particularly to the home, the same precautionary measures should be applied to the place of work. Secure or bring to the attention of appropriate personnel the kinds of apparatus that could move or fall, dangerous chemicals, and unreachable emergency shutoff switches.

During an Earthquake

If inside, STAY THERE. Get under a sturdy table or desk, (holding on to it so it doesn't "creep" away from you), or brace yourself in a doorway or corner. If you can, move to an inside hallway, and choose a location that would allow you breathing space and air in case the building should collapse around you. Stay away from windows, bookcases, china cabinets, heavy mirrors, hanging plants, and other heavy objects. Watch out as well for falling plaster, and if in the kitchen, turn off the stove at the first sign of shaking. *If you are in a crowded store or other public place*, move away from display shelves containing objects that may fall, but do not rush for exits. *In a high-rise building*, get under a desk and stay away from windows. Stay on the same floor where you are; don't use elevators, as the power may go off. There also is the strong possibility that the fire alarm or sprinkler systems may be activated.

Outside. Move away from power lines, power poles, trees, walls, and chimneys to an open area, but if you are on a sidewalk near a building, duck into the doorway to protect yourself from falling debris. *If you are in your car,* pull over to the side and stop. While the car's suspension system may make the car shake violently, it still is a safe place to be. Do NOT attempt to cross bridges or overpasses, since they may have been damaged. Even after the quake is over, and you are proceeding, avoid them. Be careful not to park under overhead wires, bridges, or overpasses. Don't get out to remove any electrical wires that may have fallen across the vehicle. STAY IN YOUR CAR until the shaking has stopped.

Special Preparations for the Elderly

During and after an earthquake, you'll need to assess your situation quickly and make every action count. Stay calm and take deep breaths. Be sure to keep away from windows or other glass. Brace yourself in a doorway or inside hallway, or lower yourself to the floor and slide under a sturdy table. If you aren't able to get to a safer area, just sit down wherever you are. Don't try to remain standing.

If you are unable to move safely and quickly, *stay where you are*, even if you are in bed. Try to protect your head and body with whatever is available—pillows, lap robe, books, your arms, or any other handy object. If you are in a wheelchair, remember to lock your wheel brakes wherever you are. Do whatever you can to protect yourself until the shaking stops. Also, if you have pets—particularly a guide or hearing dog— keep them securely harnessed or confined, as they may be frightened and try to run away. When the quake seems over and the shaking has stopped, call for help if you need it, and *don't give up*. Use your whistle or flashlight; pound on walls; go to a safe window and wave a brightly colored, high-visibility object out this window. Do anything you can to attract attention.

After the Earthquake

Stop for a moment and try to adjust to the shock, because after a major quake, there are three priorities that must be set:
• Check for injuries.
• Check for fires and gas leaks.
• Turn off the utilities if necessary.

You want to make sure that everyone with you is okay. If any are seriously injured, give first aid, but don't move them unless they are in immediate danger of further injury.

Make sure you have your shoes on (heavy ones if possible), because you need the protection from debris and broken glass. When you're doing your checking, rely on a flashlight. Do NOT use matches, electrical switches, or electrical appliances in case there is a gas leak. Shut off electrical power if you suspect damage to wiring, and make a check of water as well as gas and electricity. If you smell gas, shut off the main valve but do this *only in an emergency*. The main gas shutoff valve is next to your meter on the inlet pipe. Use a wrench and make a quarter turn in either direction so it runs crosswise on the pipe and is now closed.

If the utilities are turned off, when it is safe to turn them back on, be sure a *qualified technician* does it. Precautions like this are necessary because fires that have started from broken gas lines or electrical short-circuits are frequent causes of after-quake destruction. Also be careful NEVER to touch a downed power line, objects touched by lines, or electrical appliances broken during the quake.

Clean up any medicines or other potentially harmful materials such as bleaches, gasoline, and other flammable liquids. Make sure that sewage lines are intact before flushing the toilet. Also check the water supply. For emergency water, you can use melted ice cubes, water from toilet tanks, but NOT from those where a disinfectant chemical has been added, and NOT from the toilet bowl.

Do NOT use your phones except for emergency calls. To notify your out-of-town contact people, use mail to let them know your situation until telephone service is more readily available. By the same token, you should not drive your car unless there is an emergency—keep the streets clear for vehicles that *are* handling emergencies.

Whenever it is necessary to enter a damaged building, proceed with great caution, because aftershocks can bring them down. When you are cooking, you obviously should not use the fireplace if it has become cracked or damaged during the quake. "Make-do cooking" can be handled with camping stoves, fondue pots, or barbeques as long as there is adequate ventilation.

Keep your pets safe by confining them if the walls or fences are down.

Turn on your battery-powered radio so you will be aware of the latest reports and information. Do NOT go "sightseeing," but continue to be careful in case there are aftershocks. While most are smaller than the main event, some can be large enough to cause additional damage or bring down weakened structures.

Measuring the Intensity of the Earthquake

One of the first pieces of media information you're likely to hear about the earthquake is how it measured on the Richter scale, and a difference of just a couple of points on that scale can be tremendous. For example, a 6.0 quake has a seismic wave a hundred times as large, and releases almost a thousand times as much energy, as one measuring 4.0.

Magnitudes and results of earthquakes are as follows:

1.0 to 2.9: Probably won't be felt by most people. No damage.

3.0 to 3.9: Minor shaking, can be felt barely. No damage.

4.0 to 4.9: Tremors can be felt several miles away. Very minor damage may occur.

5.0 to 5.9: Fairly strong shaking and no doubt that it's an earthquake! Some damage will be reported.

6.0 to 6.9: A "moderate" earthquake, with widespread damage. Possible injuries or deaths will result.

7.0 to 7.75: A "major" earthquake in which most manmade structures will be damaged.

7.76 and above: A "great" earthquake in which the damage and destruction are nearly total, and almost all manmade structures are *severely* damaged.

But even with this scale, remember that the intensity of the quake may vary somewhat from one local area to the next.

Tsunamis: Linked to Major Quakes

Particularly in Pacific islands such as the Hawaiian group, and on the U.S. Pacific Coast and in Alaska, there is a need to be on the lookout for "tsunamis," which are destructive waves generated by some ocean-area earthquakes far away. As it crosses the ocean, the tsunami's length may be a hundred miles from crest to crest, and its forward speed in deep water may exceed six hundred miles per hour. Although the height at this point may be only a few feet, its wave height increases as it reaches the shoaling water of the coastlines in its destructive path. It is here that the speed decreases and the real danger appears—sometimes crests of more than a hundred feet, hitting with devastating force. One beach may get a small tsunami while another is hit by a giant.

Treat ANY tsunami warning with respect! If you hear that an earthquake has occurred, stand by for a tsunami emergency, and stay tuned to your radio or TV station.

If an earthquake strikes in your own area, it is a natural warning. Get out of low-lying coastal areas after a local earthquake.

Sometimes one gets advance warning of a tsunami by the coastal waters taking on a noticeable rise or fall. Heed the warning! Be careful never to go down to the beach "just to look at what's happening." If you can see this wave, you are too close to escape it. Unless otherwise determined by authorities, the potential danger areas are those less than fifty feet above sea level and within one mile of the coast for tsunamis of distant origin, or less than a hundred feet above sea level and within one mile of the coast for tsunamis of local origin. Warnings apply to you if you live in *any* Pacific coastal area.

Although you can't do very much to protect yourself except to have an emergency kit prepared and to move inland to higher ground *before* this tidal wave hits shore, once evacuated, you should prepare to stay in an alternate temporary shelter as long as the tsunami or storm warning is in effect, or if your home has been damaged.

When you get back to your home, beware of gas buildup. Use your flashlight, NOT matches or lanterns to check on damage. Open all the windows and doors to help the building dry out, and make sure NOT to use any food or water that has come in contact with the floodwaters.

Hurricanes

The hurricane season is between June 1 and November 30, and hurricanes are most likely to strike along the Atlantic and Gulf coasts. Since the pattern is difficult to pinpoint years in advance, people sometimes forget too soon how violent a hurricane can be and think of it as just an extra splash nudging the edge of the property. They couldn't be more mistaken. Hurricanes can be dangerous killers, provoking incredible destruction to persons and property.

If official weather warnings are ignored, it can become a tragic mistake.

If you live in a coastal area, be prepared at the start of each hurricane season. Check—and recheck, if necessary—your supply of boards, tools, batteries, nonperishable foods, and the other equipment such as flashlights, a first-aid kit, a fire extinguisher, and a battery-powered radio you would need if a hurricane should strike your area. Trim back deadwood from trees, and make sure that downspouts and rain gutters are secure.

Check the emergency services office to find out about community hurricane preparedness plans. See which areas are to be evacuated during an emergency, which ones are considered designated safe areas, and what the safe evacuation routes are to the shelter, as well as making sure that relatives and friends know your plans.

Weather Advisories

Today we are more fortunate than they were in the past about the amount of advance weather alert received. Usually the National Weather Service can provide twelve to twenty-four hours' advance warning. The "hurricane watch" means that a hurricane is a threat to coastal areas. Everyone in the area covered should listen for further advisories to see what direction the hurricane may be taking *and* be prepared to act in case a hurricane warning is issued.

A WARNING means that hurricane winds of seventy-four miles an hour or higher, or a combination of dangerously high water and very rough seas, are expected in a specific coastal area within the twenty-four hours. If you hear this, begin precautionary actions IMMEDIATELY. Don't wait until the last minute to do the things that might leave you unprepared, or even marooned. Plan what you can do in the time available, and keep calm throughout the emergency.

If you are in a mobile home, you'll want to get to more substantial shelter, because they are very vulnerable to overturning in strong winds. (Steps you can take in advance to protect your mobile home are discussed in the section on tornadoes.)

Whether you vacation or reside in a beach location, you also want to make an early departure from low-lying beach areas that may be swept by high tides or storm waves. Since some areas may flood before others, you don't want to get caught in your car by the hurricane on an open coastal road. Storm surge (that great dome of water that sweeps across the coastline near the area where the eye of the hurricane makes its landfall and acts like a bulldozer, sweeping everything in its path) and hurricane-caused flooding are erratic, so may occur with little or no warning.

Because of this, don't wait. When your local government advises evacuation, do so IMMEDIATELY. Listen to your car radio for further instructions, such as where emergency shelters will be located.

If you live in a sturdy home that is inland, away from the beaches and low-lying coastal areas, stay there and make emergency preparations UNLESS evacuation from this area has been advised, too. Just in case, however, keep your car fueled because flooding or power failures could shut down service stations.

Terms You Should Know

Tropical disturbance: A moving area of thunderstorms in the tropics that maintains its identity for twenty-four or more hours. (This is a common phenomenon in the tropics.)

Tropical depression: Rotary circulation at surface, highest constant wind speed thirty-eight miles per hour (thirty-three knots).

Tropical storm: Distinct rotary circulation; constant wind speed ranges from thirty-nine to seventy-three miles per hour (thirty-four to sixty-three knots).

Hurricane: Pronounced rotary circulation, constant wind speed of seventy-four miles per hour (sixty-four knots) or more.

Small-craft cautionary statements: When a tropical cyclone (hurricane) threatens a coastal area, small-craft operators are advised to remain in port or not to venture into the open sea.

Preparing for the Hurricane

- Moor boats securely, or evacuate them to a safer area. When the boat is moored, leave it, and don't return while the wind and waves are up.

- Board over windows, or protect them with storm shutters or tape. For small windows, the main danger comes from wind-driven debris, but larger windows may be broken by the pressure of the intense winds.

- Secure any outdoor objects that might be blown away or uprooted. This includes garbage cans, garden tools, toys, porch furniture, and signs, but there are many objects that seem completely harmless until a hurricane-force wind strikes them and they become as deadly as a wartime missile. The way to avoid this problem is to anchor them securely or store them inside BEFORE the storm makes it impossible to do.

- Move valuables to upper floors.

- Bring in pets. If you are forced to evacuate, be sure to leave food and water for them because they can't be taken with you to a shelter.

- Use the phone only for emergencies.
- Collect drinking water and store it in clean bathtubs, jugs, bottles, and cooking utensils in case the area water supply becomes contaminated or damaged by hurricane-caused floods. Before the hurricane may cut off electrical power, turn your refrigerator up to its coldest point, and don't open unless absolutely necessary.
- If you have not been advised to evacuate, stay indoors on the downwind side of the house or apartment, away from the windows. Don't be fooled by the eye of the hurricane into thinking it is over. The lull may last half an hour or only a few moments; and on the other side of the eye the winds will rise very rapidly to hit hurricane force, but come from the opposite direction.

- The combination of the high winds and the rain from hurricanes moving inland can cause severe flooding, which would make travel *extremely* dangerous at this time. You can monitor the storm's position by listening to weather advisories on the radio.

- *Especially for the elderly* (and this information refers to floods as well as hurricanes), preparedness training and a disaster plan are essential if you should become isolated at home as a result of a severe storm. It's always useful to have close at hand a lightweight drawstring bag that will contain your medications, special emergency sanitary aids, a small flashlight, and a whistle in case evacuation should be necessary. If you have impaired mobility, keep this bag tied to your wheelchair or walker. Have a "buddy system" with some relative, neighbor, or friend so that your whereabouts will be known and you are likely to get help faster. To attract this help you should use your whistle, flashlight, or any other method you can think of to direct them to your location.

In the meantime, keep calm. Listen to your radio and television. If it were just a flood, you would move to the highest point in the house. For a hurricane, stay in the *center* of the house, preferably in a small room or on the side *opposite* the direction from which the wind is blowing. Also stay alert to the need to move to a higher floor in the event of flooding.

When the hurricane has passed, be cautious in using electrical equipment in wet areas. If flooded, it should be dried and checked before being returned to service. Don't drink water from a faucet until you are told by the authorities that it

is safe. Food is something else to be extracautious about
because frequently it can be contaminated by the flood waters.
Check before using and, if so, throw it out.

After the "All Clear"

As with an earthquake, resist the temptation to sightsee the
damage. Any driving should be done in an extracareful manner
because of the possibility of dangling electric wires, low spots
that still may be flooded, and undermined roads. However, if
you do notice any broken or damaged water, sewer, or electrical line, be sure to report it right away. Preventing fires
requires universal effort because lowered water pressure could
make fire fighting difficult.

If you have been evacuated from your home and are now
returning, it is important here, as with any disaster, to check
for gas leaks, and to make sure, before using, that food and
water have not become spoiled.

Tornadoes Strike Suddenly

When a tornado is spotted, you have only a short time to
make life-or-death decisions. The "twister" is a violent windstorm characterized by an ominous black, twisting, funnel-
shaped cloud. Tornadoes occur in connection with thunderstorms and frequently are accompanied, or followed, by
lightning and sometimes heavy rain or hail. Tornadoes form at
the base of a cloudbank and form a dark, spinning column.
However, if the rain is heavy or if the tornado forms at night,
the only sign you may have is its loud, roaring noise, similar to
that of a train or a plane.

Tornadoes can strike anywhere, except the polar regions,
and in any season of the year. However, they are most likely to
occur during the midafternoon and early-evening periods, in
the months from April to October. They are most often found
in the middle western, southeastern, and northeastern parts of
the United States. They strike viciously, with their force
caused by extremely high winds and very low air pressure.
Although they normally touch ground for less than twenty
minutes, they may touch down several times in different areas,
and they spell DANGER!

What to Do

Know where the best shelter space is in your office, school, or place of work as well as in your home. Hold tornado drills in home, office, or school during the tornado season, because if you wait until a tornado is spotted, you probably won't have time to look for shelter unless you have chosen it in advance.

Watch the sky, listen to the radio for weather news, but don't call the National Weather Service unless you spot a tornado. Word of a tornado *watch* is an alert that there is the possibility of tornado development, which may stay in effect for several hours and cover an area as large as several states. During this period there is no need to change your regular routine, except to stay alert. A tornado *warning*, however, means that a tornado has been sighted and indicates its location and probable storm path during a specified time period—usually an hour or less. When this warning is given, people in the storm's path should take precautions immediately. *Seek inside shelter.*

At Home

It is preferable to go to the *lowest* level of the building, such as a basement or storm cellar, and keep emergency equipment on hand there (such as a lantern or powerful flashlight, and useful tools—a crowbar, pick, shovel, hammer, pliers, and screwdriver—in case you might need an escape route if debris should block the exits.

However, if a basement isn't available, choose an inner hallway or small inner room away from windows. Avoid anything with wide, free-span rooms, such as an auditorium, cafeteria, or large hallway. Make sure you get under something that is sturdy, such as a workbench or heavy table, and use your arms to protect your head and neck.

Mobile Homes

Mobile homes are particularly dangerous when a tornado hits down with its high winds. Frequently they overturn, although tieing down may offer *some* wind-damage protection. To tie it down, the mobile home should be properly blocked. To do this, consult a contractor and make sure that enough tie-down sets are used and properly placed, and the proper anchor and approved tensioning devices are used. Also pay special attention is paid to patio awnings, cabanas, and expando units. Even so, when a hurricane or windstorm of a tornado's intensity strikes, EVACUATE—don't stay in your mobile home.

Before this happens, find out what community shelter your mobile home park has, and what leader is responsible for constant radio monitoring during tornado-threatening or tornado-watch periods. The shelter you want to seek is a sturdy structure. If nothing like this is nearby, lie flat in the nearest ditch, ravine, or culvert, and use your hands to shield your head.

Schools Should Plan Special Precautions

When new schools are being planned, officials should keep tornadoes in mind as construction standards are set. Each school, new or old, should be inspected and tornado shelter areas designated. To make sure teachers and students know their designated shelter areas, tornado drills should be held, particularly where the threat is greatest. At this time children could be instructed that a command to assume protective postures means instant action. They should learn exactly what to

do when they hear the words "Everybody down, facing the inside wall! Crouch on elbows and knees! Hands over back of head!"

It also would be helpful to have a statewide or countywide plan to see that any tornado news gets out universally and rapidly—so children could be rounded up from the playground, and school buses kept from going out during a tornado watch.

If by any chance the bus is already out on the road, or the school building isn't of reinforced construction, quickly get the students to a nearby reinforced building or to a ravine or open ditch, and have everyone lie flat while protecting their heads.

In Stores or High-rises

If you are downtown or in a shopping mall, get off the street and go into a building. Stay away from windows and doors. Shopping centers should have predesignated shelter areas, as should nursing homes, hospitals, and factories. If they don't, interior hallways on the lowest floor usually are best.

If you are in a high-rise building, go to interior small rooms or hallways.

If you are outside, never try to outrun a tornado in a car. Tornadoes can pick a car up and throw it through the air. Get out of the car, and go inside a house or building. If none is nearby or if you're caught outside with no time to get indoors, lie in a ditch, or crouch near a strong building. Remember to cover your head with your hands. Protect yourself from flying debris in any way you can.

Emergency Information

Emergency Information Sheet
   Fill Out Your Sheet
   Special Medical Problems
   Known Drug Allergies

Telephone Emergency Information Sheets

Sample Medical Release for a Minor

Important Family Records

Important Telephone Numbers

First-Aid Kit for Your Automobile
   Help Is as Easy as 1-2-3

House Diagram

Notes

In times of crisis, it helps greatly if you can quickly and efficiently supply emergency personnel with the information they need to help you. Having such information immediately available can speed up the diagnosis and treatment—sometimes making a critically important difference. If you keep on hand an emergency information sheet and a medical identification tag (if you need one), it will make it much easier for you or your family to receive medical assistance.

Emergency Information Sheet

You'll find an emergency information sheet represented here with all the pertinent information. The sheet should provide emergency personnel with all the essential data in case you are unable to provide that information. It is wise to keep this sheet in your wallet or purse at all times.

Moreover, it is especially important that children carry such a sheet so their parents can be immediately notified in case of an emergency, for often a physician is unable to go forward with treatment until parental permission is granted.

Fill Out Your Sheet

Be sure you fill out your emergency information sheet and carry it in your wallet. The following information should be included in the medical sections:

Special Medical Problems

In this space be sure to list any important medical conditions you have that emergency personnel will need to know about. For instance, if you have a history of heart problems, that information should be included. Or if you are troubled by back problems, that, too, should be listed, so emergency personnel will know to be extra careful in case they have to move you. If you're lucky enough not to have any major problems, then simply note "none."

Known Drug Allergies

In this section list any drugs that will cause you to have an allergic reaction. Again, if you're among the fortunate ones not to have any allergy problems with drugs, simply write "none."

EMERGENCY INFORMATION SHEET

My name is _____

Home phone _____

Address _____
In case of emergency contact:

_____   _____
Name   Phone

_____   _____
Name   Phone

- -
(Fold here)

Special medical problems: _____

_____

Known drug allergies: _____

_____

Family doctor: _____

Phone: _____

EMERGENCY INFORMATION SHEET

My name is ⸻

Home phone ⸻

Address ⸻

In case of emergency contact:

⸻

Name   Phone

⸻

Name   Phone

- -

(Fold here)

Special medical problems: ⸻

⸻

Known drug allergies: ⸻

⸻

Family doctor: ⸻

Phone: ⸻

EMERGENCY INFORMATION SHEET

My name is _____

Home phone _____

Address _____
In case of emergency contact:

_____   _____
Name   Phone

_____   _____
Name   Phone

- -
(Fold here)

Special medical problems: _____

_____

Known drug allergies: _____

_____

Family doctor: _____

Phone: _____

EMERGENCY INFORMATION SHEET

My name is _____

Home phone _____

Address _____
In case of emergency contact:

_____   _____

Name   Phone

_____   _____

Name   Phone

- -
(Fold here)

Special medical problems: _____

_____

Known drug allergies: _____

_____

Family doctor: _____

Phone: _____

EMERGENCY INFORMATION SHEET

My name is _____

Home phone _____

Address _____
In case of emergency contact:

_____   _____
Name   Phone

_____   _____
Name   Phone

- -
(Fold here)

Special medical problems: _____

_____

Known drug allergies: _____

_____

Family doctor: _____

Phone: _____

Telephone Emergency Information Sheets

Here are some special information sheets prepared for you to place next to your telephone and use in times of emergency. Take the time now to fill them out with the pertinent telephone numbers and place them next to your phones—or post them in a prominent place where those in your family know to look for such important information.

Fire department _____
(Phone number)

Police _____
(Phone number)

Emergency medical _____
(Name)   (Phone number)

Physician _____
(Name)   (Phone number)

Utility Action Card

Gas _____

Electric _____

Water _____

Telephone Emergency Information Sheets

   Here are some special information sheets prepared for you to place next to your telephone and use in times of emergency. Take the time now to fill them out with the pertinent telephone numbers and place them next to your phones—or post them in a prominent place where those in your family know to look for such important information.

Fire department _____
                                    (Phone number)
Police _____
                              (Phone number)
Emergency medical _____
                         (Name)   (Phone number)
Physician _____
                 (Name)   (Phone number)

Utility Action Card

Gas _____

Electric _____

Water _____

Sample Medical Release for a Minor

In times of emergency, it is very often necessary for an authorized adult to give medical personnel permission for the treatment of a minor. Here is a sample form of such a medical release for a minor; the form will allow treatment during an emergency.

Although other means exist for emergency hospitals to get the permission they need to treat a minor, it is a very good idea to keep one of these standard permission slips on file at your child's school as well as at the child's doctor's office, and even at the nearest hospital. This precaution ensures that there will be no delay in case of an emergency. The information on the medical release should be updated annually.

Sample form:

I, _____ , parent (or

legal guardian) of _____ ,
a minor, hereby authorize any medical or surgical treatment that may be necessary in an emergency, and in my absence, for the well-being of the above-mentioned minor. I agree to hold the physician or hospital treating the above-mentioned minor harmless.

_____ has the

following allergies: _____

_____

has the following medical conditions: _____

_____

Hospitalization insurance:

Name of company _____

Policy number _____

Group number _____

Dated _____ Signed _____
                                          Parent (or legal guardian)

Sample Medical Release for a Minor

In times of emergency, it is very often necessary for an authorized adult to give medical personnel permission for the treatment of a minor. Here is a sample form of such a medical release for a minor; the form will allow treatment during an emergency.

Although other means exist for emergency hospitals to get the permission they need to treat a minor, it is a very good idea to keep one of these standard permission slips on file at your child's school as well as at the child's doctor's office, and even at the nearest hospital. This precaution ensures that there will be no delay in case of an emergency. The information on the medical release should be updated annually.

Sample form:

I, _____ , parent (or

legal guardian) of _____ ,
a minor, hereby authorize any medical or surgical treatment that may be necessary in an emergency, and in my absence, for the well-being of the above-mentioned minor. I agree to hold the physician or hospital treating the above-mentioned minor harmless.

_____ has the

following allergies: _____

_____

has the following medical conditions: _____

_____

Hospitalization insurance:

Name of company _____

Policy number _____

Group number _____

Dated _____ Signed _____
                                    Parent (or legal guardian)

Sample Medical Release for a Minor

In times of emergency, it is very often necessary for an authorized adult to give medical personnel permission for the treatment of a minor. Here is a sample form of such a medical release for a minor; the form will allow treatment during an emergency.

Although other means exist for emergency hospitals to get the permission they need to treat a minor, it is a very good idea to keep one of these standard permission slips on file at your child's school as well as at the child's doctor's office, and even at the nearest hospital. This precaution ensures that there will be no delay in case of an emergency. The information on the medical release should be updated annually.

Sample form:

I, _____ , parent (or

legal guardian) of _____ ,
a minor, hereby authorize any medical or surgical treatment that may be necessary in an emergency, and in my absence, for the well-being of the above-mentioned minor. I agree to hold the physician or hospital treating the above-mentioned minor harmless.

_____ has the

following allergies: _____

_____

has the following medical conditions: _____

_____

Hospitalization insurance:

    Name of company _____

    Policy number _____

    Group number _____

Dated _____ Signed _____
                                                              Parent (or legal guardian)

Important Family Records

Following is a list of key information to use for your important family records. You may wish to add to this list. If so, just add on any further material. Be sure to place these records in a safe location (such as a metal box or a safety deposit box).

List work or school addresses and
phone numbers of all family members:

Father's work   (name of business): _____

                   Address: _____

                   Phone: _____

Mother's work   (name of business): _____

                   Address: _____

                   Phone: _____

Other family member or friend (name): _____

                   Address: _____

                   Phone: _____

List below schools and the child/
children who attend the school(s):

Name of child/children:

1. _____

2. _____

3. _____

School 1: _____

Address: _____

Phone: _____

School 2: _____

Address: _____

Phone: _____

School 3: _____

Address: _____

Phone: _____

Policy of school 1:

Hold child ☐ Yes ☐ No

Release child ☐ Yes ☐ No

Other _____

Policy of school 2:

Hold child ☐ Yes ☐ No

Release child ☐ Yes ☐ No

Other _____

Policy of school 3:

Hold child ☐ Yes ☐ No

Release child ☐ Yes ☐ No

Other _____

Other important information:
Insurance policies

Name: _____

Policy no.: _____

Name _____

Policy no.: _____

Name and location of bank: _____

Hospitalization identification no(s).: _____

Policy no(s).: _____

_____

Family doctor: _____

Address: _____

Phone: _____

Local hospital: _____

Address: _____

Phone: _____

Social Security no(s).:

Name: _____ Soc. Sec. no.: _____

Name: _____ Soc. Sec. no.: _____

Name: _____ Soc. Sec. no.: _____

Important Telephone Numbers

Fire department: 911 or: _____

Police department: 911 or: _____

Emergency ambulance: 911 or: _____

Physician: _____

_____

_____

_____

Electric company: _____

Gas company: _____

Water company: _____

Father's work number: _____

Mother's work number: _____

Other family member: _____

(Person outside of area for family members to call and report location and condition.)

Children's work: _____

_____

Children's school: _____

_____

Poison control center: _____

Pharmacy: _____

Neighbors: _____

Insurance agent: _____

Emergency Broadcast System radio: _____

Call sign: _____

AM: _____

FM: _____

Frequency: _____

Call sign: _____

AM: _____

FM: _____

Frequency: _____

Call sign: _____

AM: _____

FM: _____

Frequency: _____

Call sign: _____

AM: _____

FM: _____

Frequency: _____

Other: _____

_____

_____

First-Aid Kit for Your Automobile

Accidents do indeed happen, so as you "expect the unexpected," you can prepare yourself to be ready for any emergency.

And as you know only too well, emergencies *do* occur! In fact, you and your family bump your way through life's little nicks and scrapes all the time. Your elderly neighbor takes a tumble down a flight of stairs, your child scrapes a knee on the playground, you cut your hand changing a tire.

It happens all the time. At home. Around town. On a trip. And on our country's highways, millions of people are injured each year in automobile accidents.

If your family counts on you to take care of them in emergencies, it's a good idea to have the American Red Cross first-aid kit on hand. Inside the kit are first-aid packets for various emergencies, with the instructions for each packet printed right on the front. So successful has the use of these first-aid kits proved that they now are standard equipment for cars and trucks in several European countries.

Help Is as Easy as 1-2-3

This kit is developed around the 1-2-3 approach to provide fast-action help when an emergency hits.
- Packet 1 is for severe bleeding and burns.
- Packet 2 is for medium wounds, cuts, and scrapes.
- Packet 3 is for small cuts and scrapes.

You determine which packet fits the particular situation and open the appropriate packet. The front of each section is clearly labeled right on the kit, and instructions are repeated—and all very clearly—on the packets. With this well-organized system, the packets won't get lost. The instructions direct you step by step, telling you precisely what to do for each emergency so you can act quickly and efficiently.

Especially useful to keep in your car, van, or camper, there is nothing that will dry out, spill, or get messy. Everything is in sealed packets that stay fresh and clean right up to the minute you use them.

The kit also includes items recommended elsewhere in this book and sometimes not included in prepackaged first-aid kits. These items include:

• scissors strong enough to cut through clothing, yet blunt-tipped to be safe around children
• triangular bandage to wrap a head wound or make an arm sling
• a rescue blanket, lightweight and waterproof, to retain the body's heat when treating for shock

Additionally, the kit itself makes a ten-by-twelve-inch pillow to put under an accident victim's head. An extra pocket allows you to customize the kit with prescription medicines and other health care items for you own family. All in all, this makes it your family's personalized first-aid kit.

The American Red Cross first-aid kit has a guarantee of satisfaction: "If you're not completely satisfied with the American Red Cross first-aid kit, return it within ten days for a complete refund."

To obtain the first-aid kit, call your local Red Cross chapter or send $24.95 plus $3.20 shipping and handling to the American Red Cross, P.O. Box D, Dept. MH, Haworth, NJ 07641 (NJ residents add 6% sales tax) allow 4 weeks for delivery.

Sample Floor Plan

KEY

1. Exits ◀ doors ⇧ windows
2. Utility cut-off: Ⓖ Ⓔ Ⓦ
   (Gas, Electric, Water)
3. First Aid Kit: ✚
4. Emergency Supplies ✳
5. Fire Extinguisher: ●
6. Reunion Place: ★

(This page can be cut or torn out of book.)

American Red Cross

Our EMERGENCY Floor Plan

American Red Cross

KEY

1. Exits ◆ doors ◇ windows
2. Utility cut-off: Ⓖ Ⓔ Ⓦ
   (Gas, Electric, Water)
3. First Aid Kit: ✚
4. Emergency Supplies ✳
5. Fire Extinguisher: ●
6. Reunion Place: ★

(This page can be cut or torn out of book.)

Date: _____

Notes

Notes

Notes

Notes